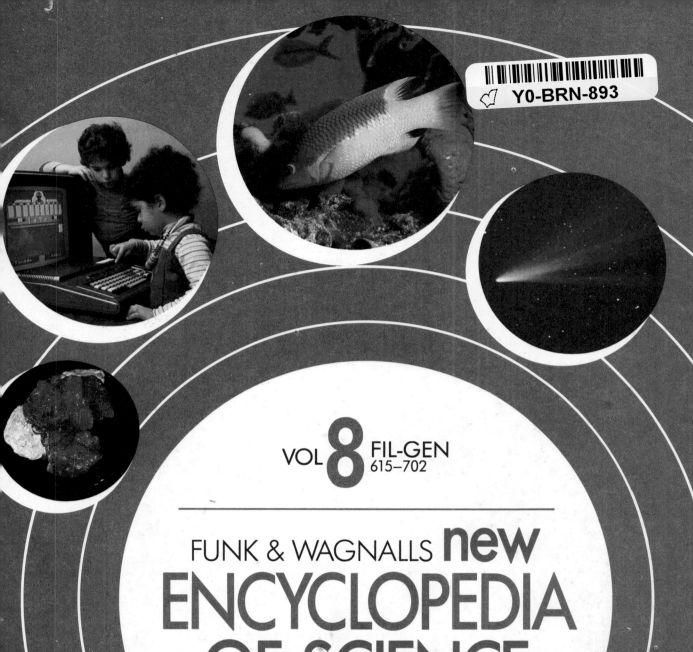

VOL **8** FIL-GEN
615–702

FUNK & WAGNALLS **new**
ENCYCLOPEDIA
OF SCIENCE

FUNK & WAGNALLS, INC.

HOW TO USE FUNK & WAGNALLS NEW ENCYCLOPEDIA OF SCIENCE

Volumes 1 through 21 have information printed on the front covers, spine, and title pages that make it easy to find the articles you want to read.
- Volume numbers are printed in all three places in Volumes 1 through 21.
- Letter breaks — $\frac{COL}{DIA}$ — are printed in all three places in Volumes 1 through 21. The letters above the line are the first three letters of the first article title in the volume. The letters below the line are the first three letters of the last article title in the volume.
- Page breaks — $\frac{351}{438}$ — are printed on the spines and title pages of Volumes 1 through 21. They provide the page numbers of the first and last text pages in the volume.

Articles are arranged alphabetically by title in Volumes 1 through 21. Most titles are printed in **BOLD-FACE CAPITAL** letters. Some titles are printed in even larger letters.
- Some titles are not article titles, but refer you to the actual article title. Within articles you will find *See* or *See also* other article names for further information. All of these references to other articles are called cross-references.
- Most article titles are followed by a phonetic pronunciation. Use the Pronunciation Guide on page vi of Volume 1 to learn the correct pronunciation of the article title.
- At the end of most articles are two sets of initials. The first set identifies the person who wrote the article. The second set identifies the special consultant who checked the article for accuracy. All of these people are listed by their initials and full names and position on pages v and vi of Volume 1.
- ◪ This symbol at the end of an article indicates that there is a project based on the subject of the article in the Projects, Bibliography & Index volume. The project is found under its article title, and all of the project article titles are arranged alphabetically on pages 1 through 64 of the Projects, Bibliography & Index volume.

The Projects, Bibliography & Index Volume contains three sections. Each is an essential part of the encyclopedia.
- Projects based on articles in the encyclopedia are found in the first section. Each is both entertaining and educational. Each is designed for use by a student and for parental participation if desired.
- Bibliography reading lists in the second section list books under general scientific categories that are also titles of major articles. Each book listed is marked with either a YA (Young Adult) or J (Juvenile) reading level indicator. YA generally applies to readers at the junior high level or higher. J applies to readers at grade levels below junior high school.
- Index entries for all article titles plus many subjects that are not article titles are found in the third section. Instructions on using the Index are found at the start of the Index section in the Projects, Bibliography & Index volume.

The filberts are 15 species of trees that belong to genus *Corylus* of the birch family. The male flowers are in long catkins that appear during the winter.

FILBERT (fil′ bərt) The filberts are a group of 15 species of trees and shrubs that belong to genus *Corylus* of the birch family. They have large, oval, deciduous leaves with toothed margins. (*See* DECIDUOUS TREE.) The leaves alternate on the stem. The male flowers are in long catkins that appear in the winter. (*See* CATKIN.) The female flowers are much smaller and grow in clusters. Each female flower has two red stigmas. (*See* FLOWER.) Both sexes are on one plant. (*See* MONOECIOUS.) Filberts vary in height from 3 to 36 m [10 to 120 ft].

The filbert plants produce edible nuts also called filberts. These nuts are roundish and about 2.5 cm [1 in] long. Until fairly recently, members of genus *Corylus* were called hazels. The nuts are still often called hazelnuts. Forked branches from the American filbert (*Corylus americana*) were once used as "divining rods." According to tradition, these "divining rods" could be used to find underground water. *See also* BIRCHES.

A.J.C./M.H.S.

FILTER (fil′ tər) A filter is a device used to remove solid particles in liquids and gases. Filter paper, a porcelain disk, or a series of perforated plates are all examples of filters. All filters have tiny channels or holes. These allow the gas or liquid to pass through but they are too small to allow solid particles to pass through. A cake of the solid builds up on the filter. This cake has to be removed from time to time. Pressure may be needed to force the

Below, a rotary disk filter collects deposits from industrial liquids passed through it. Below left, banks of air filters remove trace quantities of radioactive material from the air at nuclear power stations and at factories handling radioactive isotopes.

Left, the Buchner flask is used to speed up filtration in laboratories. The rubber pipe connects to a vacuum pump.

In physics, the word filter means something very different. It is a device that is used to separate out certain colors from light. (*See* SPECTRUM.) White light is a mixture of different colors. A filter allows only one color to pass through it. All the other colors are absorbed by the filter. Color filters are used in photography and in lighting.   M.E./A.D.

FILTER FEEDING (fil′ tər fēd′ ing) Filter feeding is a method by which many water-dwelling animals obtain food. Filter feeding animals stay still while straining food out of the water. Bivalves are the best known filter feeders. A water current is drawn in through the bivalve. The food particles are trapped by a slimy substance on the gills. Many annelids and crustaceans are also filter feeders.
J.M.C./R.J.B.

gas or liquid through the filter. Sometimes a pump is used to suck the gas or liquid through. Frequently a liquid may simply drip through the filter under the force of gravity.

Filtering is vital to industry and science for purifying materials. Filters are used in water installations to purify the water supply. They remove dust from the air in air conditioning systems. Factory chimneys are fitted with filters. They remove particles from waste gases and so reduce pollution in the air. Vacuum cleaners use filters to trap the dust that they suck in.

In these examples, a gas or liquid is purified by removing unwanted particles. Sometimes, a filter is used to trap particles that are important. Precious metals can be separated from other materials by filtering. Prospectors do this when they are panning for gold. Filters are used in medical laboratories to separate bacteria and viruses from infected material. The size of the holes in these filters is known exactly. This allows microorganisms of a particular size to be filtered off and examined. This method is also used in hospitals to produce sterile liquids. (*See* STERILIZATION.) Sterile liquids contain no bacteria at all.

Bullfinch

Above, the brightly colored bullfinch, a member of the finch family Fringillidae.

FINCH (finch) A finch is a songbird that belongs to the finch family Fringillidae, the largest family of North American birds. They grow 10 to 17.5 cm [4 to 7 in] in length. Finches have short, heavy bills with which they crack seeds. These seeds are their main source of food when they are not nesting. Male finches are very colorful. Females are usually a dull brown. Some of these birds fly in flocks and migrate long distances. Finches are found from cool temperate areas to the tropics. *See also* GROSBEAK; SPARROW.

S.R.G./L.L.S.

FIR (fər) The fir is a coniferous tree that belongs to the pine family Pinaceae. There are six species in North America, including the Douglas fir, one of the largest trees in the world. It grows up to 75 m [250 ft] in height. Firs grow in cold, mountainous regions. Large forests of fir are cut for their valuable timber. The resin from the Balsam fir is used as a strong, clear glue. *See also* PINE FAMILY; SPRUCE.

S.R.G./M.H.S.

The Douglas fir is a member of the pine family and is one of the largest trees in the world, growing up to 75 m [250 ft] in height. This fir is widely grown in temperate regions and is known for its valuable timber.

FIRE (fīr) Fire is the heat and light that come from burning materials. A material that burns is one that can combine quickly with the oxygen in the air. Burning, then, is a rapid process of oxidation. Most materials that burn are made up of chemical compounds containing large amounts of carbon and hydrogen. Combustion is another name for burning. In 1774, Antoine Lavoisier, a French chemist, discovered the essential part played by oxygen in combustion.

Some substances combine with oxygen extremely slowly. No light and very little heat are produced. Rusting is an example of slow oxidation. (*See* RUST.)

Before the chemical reaction called fire can occur, certain conditions must be met. First, a substance that can burn must be present. Such a substance is called a fuel. Wood makes good fuel. Water does not. Second, a good supply of oxygen must be present. The oxygen usually comes from the air. Third, the fuel must be treated until it reaches its ignition temperature. The ignition temperature is also called the kindling point. The kindling point is the temperature at which the fuel can easily combine with oxygen. Until matches were invented, fires were started by borrowing wood or coal from another fire. If no fire was nearby, a pile of twigs could be set afire with sparks. The sparks were produced by striking metal against flint. Flint is a hard stone.

Some substances, such as paper, have low kindling points. Some fuels, such as coal, must be heated considerably before they can burn. The chemical called white phosphorus must be kept under water at normal temperature. If not, it bursts into flame.

Fire has been used by people long before history was written. In prehistoric times, fire kept people warm and protected them from dangerous animals. Fire also provided light and cooked food. Human beings are the only animals that ever created and used fire.

Today, we use fire to heat water to make steam. Steam is used to run hundreds of different kinds of engines. Fire is used in thousands of ways by industry, such as in making steel and in separating metals from their ores. Fire from burning gasoline, oil, or jet fuel powers automobiles, boats, and airplanes.

Besides the countless number of beneficial ways in which fire is used, it can also be very harmful when it gets out of control. Fire has destroyed homes and other buildings. It can ruin entire towns, huge forests, and prairies. Fire prevention is a big job. There are more than 1,000,000 fire fighters in the United States. Modern buildings are built so that they cannot easily catch on fire. (*See* FIRE PROTECTION.) J.J.A./A.D.

Above, the firefly produces light by means of a substance called luciferin.

FIREFLY (fīr′ flī) A firefly, or lightning bug, is any of about 2,000 species of beetles that produce light—without heat—from special organs on their abdomens. (*See* BIOLUMINESCENCE.) The light is produced by the oxidation of a chemical called luciferin in the presence of an enzyme, ATP, and magnesium. The firefly can control the production of light. Therefore, it can control the length and rhythm of the flashes from its abdomen. Different species produce different colored lights at different rhythms. In the adult, this attracts a mate of the same species. If the female is wingless, the male is able to find her by following her flashing lights.

Fireflies range in length from 4 to 11 mm [0.2 to 0.5 m]. Most are dark brown or black with bright, contrasting colors on the thorax.

Since fireflies are bad-tasting to birds and other predators, their coloration and flashing lights probably warn these enemies to stay away. (*See* WARNING COLORATION.) The eggs, larvae, and pupae of some species are also faintly bioluminescent. The larvae feed on snails, earthworms, and insects. The adults, however, do not eat at all.

Most fireflies live in tropical or in humid, temperate areas. Most are nocturnal and rest on plants during the day. The females of some species are wingless and look like larvae. Since they are bioluminescent, they are often called glowworms. A.J.C./J.E.R.

FIRE PROTECTION (fīr′ prə tek′ shən) Fire protection is the control and extinguishing of fires. About 2½ million fires are reported to fire departments in the United States each year. The fires cause about 8,000 deaths and billions of dollars worth of damage. More than a fourth of all people killed or injured in fires are children. Sometimes, fire can destroy an entire city. In 1871, a fire swept through the city of Chicago. It destroyed 18,000 buildings and resulted in the death of 300 people. During World War II, firebombs dropped on German cities started fires which destroyed large areas of the cities.

One of the chief hazards of fire is toxic smoke. Many man-made substances, such as plastics and chemicals, give off toxic fumes when they burn. If inhaled, the smoke can have harmful effects on the lungs. Dense, heavy smoke can cause asphyxiation (death or unconsciousness because of lack of oxygen).

Carelessness with matches and cigarette stubs is one of the chief causes of fire. Fires in the home are often caused by defective electrical wiring. Many fires start in kitchens when cooking oils and fats become ignited. Improper storage of flammable liquids, like gasoline and cleaning fluids, is another cause

Facing right, fire is one of humanity's most useful tools when properly controlled.

of fires in the home. Gasoline, for example, should never be kept in a plastic container. It should be stored in a metal container and placed in a cool spot.

Fires can be prevented, or slowed down, by fireproof materials like asbestos, brick, stone, and chemically treated wood and fabrics. Asbestos, for example, does not burn. It was widely used in different kinds of building materials, until medical researchers discovered that the fibers can cause lung cancer. Now, substitute fireproof materials are being developed. Wood and plastics that are treated with fire retardant chemicals are difficult to ignite. They burn slowly. Special paints help retard the spread of fire. Steel fireproof doors are used in most large buildings to keep fires from spreading. Most public buildings have automatic sprinkler systems. Nozzles located in room ceilings spray water when the temperature in the room rises above a certain point. Many homes now have smoke detectors. These are battery-powered devices that sound an alarm when there is smoke in the room.

Fire extinguishers are provided by law in public buildings, factories, and schools. Most fire extinguishers consist of a metal container filled with chemicals and/or water. The most common extinguisher is the soda-acid type. It sprays a mixture of water and carbon dioxide gas on fires. Soda-acid extinguishers are not effective against gasoline, oil, and electrical fires. Foam extinguishers must be used on these fires. Foam extinguishers spray a heavy, white chemical foam that smothers the fire by depriving it of oxygen. Another type of extinguisher that is used on oil and electrical fires contains carbon dioxide under pressure. Here, too, the carbon dioxide gas smothers the flames.

Fire escapes are steel stairways mounted on the outside of multi-story buildings. They are required by law on most older multi-story buildings. New multi-story buildings are required to have enclosed concrete stairways that can be sealed off from other parts of the building. This is because elevators do not

Fire fighters (below) are shown using water to extinguish a fire.

always work during fires. Most large buildings have fire alarm systems that ring bells to alert the occupants. Some alarm systems automatically alert the local fire department.

Public buildings are inspected regularly by local fire departments for fire hazards. Fire fighters give talks and demonstrations at schools to educate children to the dangers of fire. Chambers of commerce and other civic groups promote fire prevention through newspaper and television appeals. Every year, in the week preceeding October 9, the U.S. celebrates National Fire Prevention Week. October 9th is the anniversary of the Chicago Fire.

The first fire protection laws were passed in ancient Rome. In 18 B.C., Augustus set maximum heights for houses, and minimum thicknesses for walls. He also banned smoking chimneys.

Large fires are the responsibility of public fire departments. They are summoned to the scene of a fire by signals from fire alarm boxes. Fire alarm boxes are electrical devices mounted on poles at street corners. Sometimes, fire departments are notified of a fire by telephone.

Fire departments usually have three kinds of trucks: ladder trucks, pumpers, and rescue trucks. Ladder trucks have long, metal extension ladders that can reach as high as 30 meters [100 ft], or eight stories. Another type, called the snorkel, has a cagelike platform mounted on a telescoping boom. A fireman rides on the platform, and operates a high-pressure water nozzle. The boom can extend hydraulically to 46 m [150 ft]. Pumpers contain large pumps that increase the pressure of water from hydrants and other sources. The pumps force water through long hoses under high pressure. This allows firemen to direct powerful streams of water on fires from safe distances. Pumpers usually deliver from 3,000 to 6,000 liters [792 to 1,583 gal] per minute. Pumpers also contain several sizes of hoses for different types of fires. For example

small diameter hoses are used on brush fires and grass fires. Rescue trucks contain special tools for special jobs. They carry oxyacetylene torches for cutting through metal, and hydraulic jacks for lifting heavy objects. They also carry scuba gear, fire resistant suits, and emergency medical supplies and equipment. Rescue trucks are summoned for other emergencies besides fires.

Firemen wear special clothing to protect themselves against flames, falling objects, and other hazards. They wear heavy, waterproof, knee-length coats made of flame-retardant fabric. Other clothing includes helmets, gloves, and boots. Firemen also use self-contained breathing devices that allow them to breathe in smoke-filled buildings.

Airports have their own kind of fire trucks called crash trucks. Crash trucks are pumpers that spray foam or dry chemicals on burning airplanes. Water is ineffective against most

An asbestos suit allows a fire fighter to walk through flames unharmed. The silvered surface of the suit reflects the heat and keeps the wearer cool and safe.

aircraft fires. Fireboats are boats used to fight fires on ships, piers, and waterfront buildings. Fireboats have pumps that draw water from rivers, lakes, and oceans. The water is directed onto the fire by large, gunlike nozzles. Large fireboats can pump 40,000 liters [10,554 gal] of water per minute.

W.R.P./R.W.L.

FISH (fish) Fish are cold-blooded, vertebrate animals. They belong to the class Pisces. (*See* COLD-BLOODED ANIMAL.) Fish first evolved about 500 million years ago. Many fossils of fish have been found. During the Devonian period—the Age of Fish—many types of fish appeared. Most have now become extinct, but about 20,000 species have survived until the present day. Three groups of fish evolved from the ancient fish: the jawless fish, the cartilaginous fish, and the bony fish.

The ostracoderms were the earliest fishes, living from about 500 million years ago.

Jawless fish   These primitive fish belong to the class Agnatha. Most of them are parasitic. (*See* PARASITE.) They do not have true jaws, but have suckerlike mouths with which to attach to other fish. These fish also do not have a true backbone or bones. Their skeleton is composed of cartilage. The group includes the hagfish and lamprey. Hagfish are saltwater scavengers of other fish. Many lampreys are saltwater fish parasites, but these species are also anadromous. They return to freshwater to spawn. (*See* SPAWNING.) Other lampreys are not parasitic. They enter freshwater streams to spawn. There are three species of hagfish and 14 species of lampreys in North America.

Above, the reef whaler shark.

Cartilaginous fish   Cartilaginous fish belong to the class Chondrichthyes. These fish do not have any true bones in their bodies. (*See* BONE.) Instead, their skeletons are made up of cartilage. Their bodies are covered with small pointed scales, which make the skin rough like sandpaper. Although cartilaginous fish are evolutionarily more modern than the jawless fish, they are more primitive than the bony fish.

The cartilaginous fish include many species of sharks, rays, and skates. The largest of all living fish is the whale shark, which may reach a length of 18.9 m [60 ft]. Although most sharks are carnivorous, some eat plankton. (*See* CARNIVORE.) Some sharks must always be moving. They are unable to pump water across their gills. They swim with their mouths opened so that a fresh supply of water is always entering. Their gills extract oxygen in the water. Modern bony fish take water into their mouths, force it over the gills and out through the openings of the gill covers. The fish are capable of doing this while the body is motionless.

Rays have flat bodies, from top to underside. Most of them live close to the ocean bottom where they feed mostly on crabs and invertebrates such as worms. Some rays, like the manta ray or devil fish, live near the surface and feed on plankton and tiny fish.

Right, the blenny is well camouflaged and could easily be mistaken for a rock.

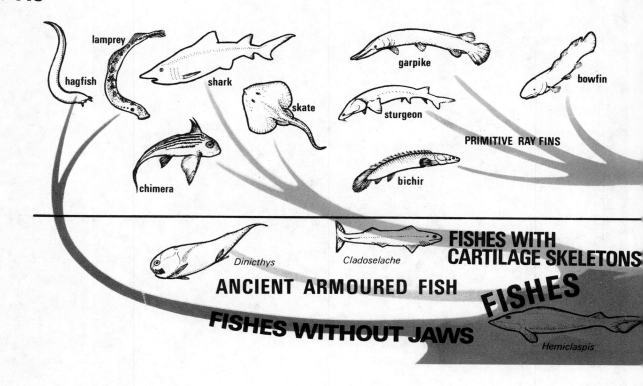

hagfish

lamprey

shark

skate

chimera

garpike

sturgeon

bichir

bowfin

PRIMITIVE RAY FINS

Dinicthys

Cladoselache

FISHES WITH CARTILAGE SKELETONS

ANCIENT ARMOURED FISH

FISHES

FISHES WITHOUT JAWS

Hemiclaspis

Above, the giant arthrodira, an extinct armored fish which lived 350 million years ago.

Above, the mullet is a marine fish which lives in coastal waters.

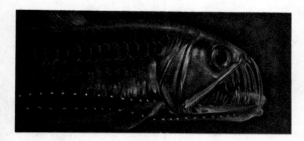

Above, the viper fish is a deep sea fish which lives between 450 and 2,700 m [1,500 and 9,000 ft] down. It grows to about 25 cm [10 in] in length.

Above, the freshwater pike has formidable teeth and will eat frogs and small water birds as well as other fish.

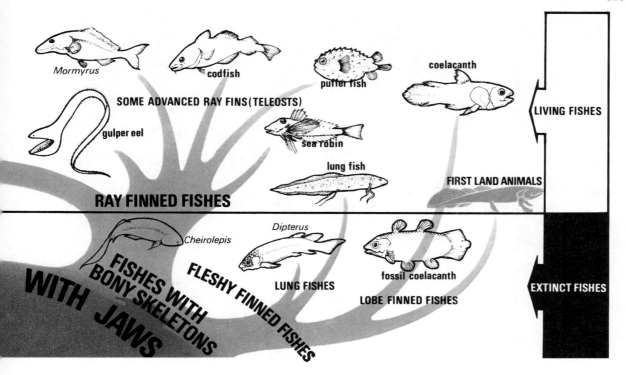

Mormyrus

codfish

puffer fish

coelacanth

SOME ADVANCED RAY FINS (TELEOSTS)

gulper eel

sea robin

LIVING FISHES

lung fish

RAY FINNED FISHES

FIRST LAND ANIMALS

Cheirolepis

Dipterus

fossil coelacanth

FISHES WITH BONY SKELETONS

FLESHY FINNED FISHES

LUNG FISHES

LOBE FINNED FISHES

WITH JAWS

EXTINCT FISHES

A typical bony fish cut away to show the arrangement of the internal organs. 1. Backbone, 2. Swim bladder, 3. Trunk muscles, 4. Ovary, 5. Intestine, 6. Stomach, 7. Heart, 8. Gills.

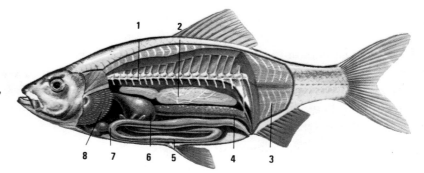

Bony fish   Bony fish are relatively modern fish that belong to the class Osteichthyes. They have a skeleton made up of bones. This group includes most of the freshwater fish and a large number of the saltwater fish. There are many different types of bony fish but most of them have scales covering their bodies, gills covered by the gill cover known as operculum, a mouth at the front of the body, a swim bladder used for buoyancy, and fins. *See also* EVOLUTION.   S.R.G./E.C.M.

FISSION (fish′ ən) An atom has at its center a core called the nucleus. Sometimes the nucleus can break into two parts that are roughly the same size. This breaking up of a nucleus is called nuclear fission. When this happens, large amounts of energy are released. (*See* ENERGY.) If the fission is controlled, this energy can be used as a source of power. This happens in nuclear power stations. If the fission is uncontrolled, the energy can be used to create an atomic explosion.

Fission can be caused by a nucleus being hit by a neutron. A neutron is a small subatomic particle. A heavy nucleus is usually

The Japanese city of Hiroshima was the first town to suffer the destructive force of nuclear fission. The bomb, dropped on August 6, 1945, killed 80,000 people by blast or radiation.

very unstable and is easily split by a collision. The mass of a heavy nucleus is greater than the combined mass of the fission fragments. (*See* MASS.) Therefore, when the nucleus is split some of its mass disappears. The missing mass is converted into energy. Albert Einstein was the first person to discover that mass can be converted into energy. A very small mass converts to a large amount of energy. Much of this energy is given off as large quantities of heat, and as high velocity particles.

A material often used in fission is an isotope of uranium. It is called uranium-235. When the nucleus of a uranium atom is struck, it usually splits into two smaller nuclei. The nucleus also releases two or three neutrons. These neutrons then collide with other nuclei and cause further fission. The reaction quickly accelerates and is called a chain reaction. If it is uncontrolled, the process leads to an atomic explosion. This was used in the atomic bomb that was dropped on Hiroshima in 1945. (*See* CHAIN REACTION; NUCLEAR WEAPON.) In a nuclear reactor, the fission process is controlled. This is done by removing some of the neutrons that are given off. This stops an explosive chain reaction from occurring. The neutrons are removed by ab-

sorbing them in rods. These rods are usually made of cadmium or boron. Not too many neutrons can be absorbed, however, otherwise the reaction will stop. The rods are inserted or removed to make sure that the reaction is going at the right speed.

Nuclear reactors are used in nuclear power stations. The heat of the reaction is converted into another form of energy—electricity. Large amounts of energy are produced in this way. For example, 1.5 million kg [3.3 million lb] of coal are needed to produce the same amount of energy as one kg [2.2 lb] of uranium-235.   M.E./J.T.

FITCH, JOHN (1743–1798) John Fitch (fich) was an American inventor who designed and built the first steamboat. In 1787 Fitch demonstrated his steam-powered vessel on the Delaware River, near Philadelphia. Although Fitch was the first person to produce a workable steamboat, he did not receive credit for starting the Steamboat Age. That honor went to Robert Fulton, another American. Twenty years after Fitch had introduced his steamboat, Fulton built one of his own design. He called it the Clermont, and successfully tested it on the Hudson River in New York.

Fitch's steamboat was propelled by six paddles on each side, like Indian canoe paddles. The paddles were driven by a steam engine. Fitch, however, had constant financial troubles. He was never able to attract enough public support for his steamboats. In 1790 he built another steamboat and placed it in regular passenger service between Philadelphia and Burlington, New Jersey. Unfortunately, there was not enough demand for passage to make the idea pay.

Fitch, who was born in Windsor Township, Connecticut, finally gave up on his steamboat efforts, and moved to Kentucky where he later died. Before his steamboat days, Fitch was a successful brassworker and silversmith in Trenton, N.J. He also served as a lieutenant in the Revolutionary War.

W.R.P./D.G.F.

FJORD (fē ȯrd′) A fjord is a long, narrow inlet of the sea. Fjords are the result of erosion and glaciation. Millions of years ago, rivers cut valleys through rock. Later, during the Ice Age, these valleys were deepened by glaciers. When the glaciers retreated, the sea level rose and flooded these deep valleys, forming fjords.

Fjords are usually very deep and often have steep walls with waterfalls. They are common along the coasts of Norway, Greenland, Alaska, and New Zealand. *See also* GLACIATION; GLACIERS AND ICE SHEET.

J.M.C./W.R.S.

FLAGELLATE (flaj′ ə lət) A flagellate is any of several primitive microorganisms that have one or more whiplike flagella. (*See* FLAGELLUM.) Though most flagellates are Protozoans, some are algae. These organisms use flagella to swim about through the water or other liquid medium in which they live. Algal flagellates contain chlorophyll and are able to carry on photosynthesis. Some have thin, protective, outer coverings of cellulose.

There are four basic types of flagellates, based on their lifestyles. Free-living flagellates, such as Euglena and Chlamydomonas,

live by themselves and usually contain chloroplasts (bodies containing chlorophyll). Colonial flagellates, such as volvox, live in an attached group and move about by collectively waving their flagella. Planktonic flagellates are a part of plankton, a vital food for many sea animals. Noctiluca is a bioluminescent planktonic flagellate that exists in such large numbers that it often causes the "white fire" seen at sea. Parasitic flagellates usually live in the blood or intestines of a mammal host, and cause serious diseases. (*See* PARASITE.) Trypanosomes are parasitic flagellates which live in human blood and cause sleeping sickness.

A.J.C./C.S.H.

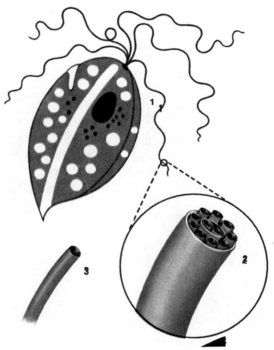

1. A flagellate named *Trichomonas*, which is a microscopic parasite in human beings. 2. A section of one flagellum of *Trichomonas*, highly magnified. 3. A section of a flagellum of a bacterium, also highly magnified. Bacteria flagella are composed of one protein fiber.

FLAGELLUM (flə jel′ əm) A flagellum is a hairlike structure extending from a cell. It is usually used for movement through water or another liquid. The structure of a flagellum is much like that of a cilium. With the exception of the bacterial flagellum, all flagella have a circle of nine fibers surrounding two other fibers. Although most flagellated organisms have one or two flagella, some have many which are easily confused with cilia.

Many protozoans and some algae have flagella. (*See* FLAGELLATES.) The gametes, or sex cells, of some algae, fungi, slime molds, and mosses also have flagella. Some lower invertebrates, such as the sponges and the Cnideria, use flagella to create a stream of water through their bodies for circulation and respiration. Some bacteria have a single flagellum that is composed of only one protein molecule. The sperm of many animals, including human beings, have flagella to allow them to swim to and fertilize an egg. (*See* FERTILIZATION; REPRODUCTION.)

A.J.C./E.R.L.

The flamingo feeds by moving its beak from side to side through the mud. Fine hairlike structures at the sides of the beak filter food from the water.

FLAMINGO (flə min′ gō) A flamingo is a tall bird that belongs to the family Phoenicopteridae. It has very long legs and a long slender neck. Flamingos wade in shallow water, feeding on small animals and plants. The American flamingo is the only species of flamingo in North America. It is occasionally seen in Florida. This bird grows to 105 cm [42 in] tall, with red to pink feathers. The color of the feathers comes from a chemical found in many marine crustaceans which the flamingo eats. If the flamingo stops eating them, it will turn white.

S.R.G./M.L.

The very young sole is much the same shape as other young fish. As it grows, it flattens out and the left eye moves to the right side of the head.

FLATFISH (flat′ fish′) A flatfish is a saltwater fish that belongs to the order Pleuronectiformes. Flounder, sole, halibut, plaice, and turbot are types of flatfishes. They are called flatfishes because their bodies have a flat shape like a pancake. Perhaps the most interesting thing about these fishes is that both of their eyes are on one side of their head. When flatfishes hatch from their eggs, they look like most other fishes, with an eye on each side. Soon, however, one side of their skull grows faster than the other. This pushes one eye over to the other side and twists the mouth. After this happens, the flatfish begins to lie on the sea floor on its blind side—the side with no eyes.

There are three families of flatfishes. The family Bothidae contains the left-sided flounders—those fishes with their eyes on the left side. Pleuronectidae contains right-sided flounders—those fish with their eyes on the right side. Soleidae contains the sole, which are right-sided. Most of these flatfishes live on the bottom of shallow, coastal waters. They eat bottom-dwelling animals. They cannot swim very well, but they can escape enemies by camouflaging themselves by adapting colors of the surrounding bottom, or burying themselves in sand. (*See* CAMOUFLAGE.) Many species are important food fishes and commercially valuable.   S.R.G./E.C.M.

FLATWORM *See* PLATHYHELMINTHES.

FLAX *See* FIBER.

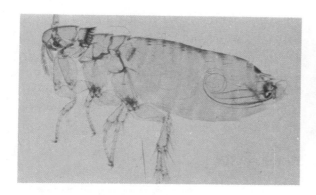

The flea is a parasitic insect which lives on the blood of other animals. Fleas can jump relatively great distances with their strong hindlegs.

FLEA (flē) A flea is any one of 1,400 species of tiny parasitic insects belonging to the order Siphonaptera. (*See* PARASITE.) Fleas have brown, wingless bodies which are flattened on the sides, and short antennae. Their long hindlegs are very strong and enable fleas to jump great distances. The common human flea, *Pulex irritans,* is only about 3 mm [0.1 in] long, yet it is able to jump more than 330 mm [13 in]. Fleas suck blood from a host by using their sharp, beaklike mouth parts, but do not feed continuously. They may live for more than a year without eating. Although most fleas will bite hosts of several species, some are parasites on only one specific type of mammal or bird.

After having sucked blood from a host, a female flea may lay hundreds of eggs on or near the host. The larvae are rarely parasitic. The process of metamorphosis may take less than a month or more than a year. Aside from the fact that they are irritating pests, fleas spread disease. Bubonic plague and typhus are spread by the rat flea (*Xenopsylla cheopis*) and other species.

The common cat flea (*Ctenocephalides felis*) and the common dog flea (*Ctenocephalides canis*) sometimes bite human beings and may transmit disease-causing tapeworms.   A.J.C./J.E.R.

Sir Alexander Fleming is shown in a laboratory checking some cultures.

FLEMING, SIR ALEXANDER (1881–1955) Sir Alexander Fleming (flem′ ing) discovered penicillin, which was the first antibiotic drug. In 1928, he was studying bacteria and noticed that some of his experiments were spoiled because the bacteria were dying. Instead of throwing them away he decided to try and find out what was killing the germs. There was a mold, called *Penicillium notatum,* growing where the bacteria had died. Fleming found out that this mold made a substance that killed germs. He called the substance penicillin. It took ten years to find a way of getting a large amount of pure penicillin from the mold. Howard Florey and Ernst Chain discovered how to do this.

Penicillin was first used to cure a sick person in 1941. Fleming, Florey, and Chain shared the Nobel Prize for Medicine in 1945 for this work. *See also* ANTIBIOTICS; PENICILLIN.   C.M./D.G.F.

FLICKER (flik′ ər) Flickers are birds that are members of the woodpecker family Picidae. There are three species in North America. The yellow-shafted flicker is common in the eastern half of the continent. The red-shafted flicker is common in the western half of the continent. The gilded flicker is common in a small area of southwestern United States and northwestern Mexico. Flickers grow to 25 cm [10 in] long. They search for insects on the ground and in trees, and nest in holes in trees.   S.R.G./M.L.

Howard Florey shared the Nobel prize for medicine in 1945 for his work in developing penicillin.

FLOREY, HOWARD WALTER (1898–1968) Howard Florey (flō′ rē) was born in Australia. He worked in Britain on the study of diseases. Florey was one of the scientists who discovered how to get pure penicillin from the mold that makes it. He shared the 1945 Nobel Prize for Medicine with Sir Ernst Chain and Sir Alexander Fleming for this work. Florey was knighted in 1944 and made Baron Florey of Adelaide in 1968. *See also* ANTIBIOTICS; PENICILLIN.   C.M./D.G.F.

FLOUNDER   *See* FLATFISH.

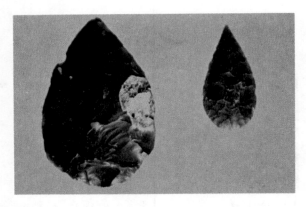

People in prehistoric times used flint to make arrowheads and other tools. Flint is hard , yet easy to chip and shape. Flint was also used in prehistoric times to make a spark for lighting fires.

FLINT (flint) Flint is a form of silica (SiO_2). Other forms of silica include agate, opal, and quartz. Flint is most often found in the form of fine-grained, dark-gray lumps in chalk and limestone. After it has been exposed to weathering, flint usually changes color to yellow or brown. It is easy to chip, and can be shaped into pieces with sharp edges. In prehistoric times, people valued flint because of this property. They made spears, knives, and arrowheads from flint. Later, people learned that flint gave a spark when it was struck against some hard metal. They began using flint to start fires. Today, the primary use of flint is for abrasives. *See also* ABRASIVE.
                                    J.J.A./R.H.

FLOWER

The flower (flaùr′) is the structure in all angiosperms (flowering plants) that is responsible for sexual reproduction. Its function is to produce seeds which will grow into new plants. There are at least 200,000 kinds of flowers, ranging in size from the microscopic duckweed blossom at 0.4 mm [0.016 in] in diameter to the tropical *Rafflesia arnoldi* at 90 cm [3 ft] in diameter. Flowers may be any of hundreds of shapes and colors. Most flowers have a distinctive fragrance to attract birds and insects needed to help with pollination. (*See* DISPERSION OF PLANTS.) Flower fossils

Facing right, the larger purple flowers are morning glory and the smaller pink are oleander.

have been found that date back more than 125,000,000 years. Flowers grow everywhere in the world except in ice-covered areas near the poles, and in the open seas. Some flowers grow wild, while others are cultivated by florists and gardeners. In the United States alone, there are more than 32,000 kinds of wild flowers.

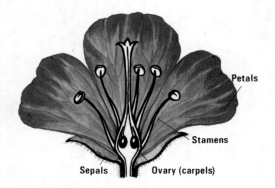

Above, a cross-section of a field geranium shows the parts of the flower.

Parts of a flower The flower consists of a number of highly modified leaves which are clustered together at the tip of a stalk. The flower parts are all attached to an enlarged section of the stalk called the receptacle. There are four whorls, or circular sets, of parts growing from the receptacle: the calyx, the corolla, the stamens, and the pistils. The calyx is made of several green, leaflike sepals which protect the developing flower bud. In some cases, the sepals may be brightly colored. The corolla is made of several, usually brightly colored, petals. The petals may take any of several shapes, or may not be present, depending on the species. The calyx and corolla together form the perianth.

Inside the perianth are the reproductive structures of the flower. The stamens are the male reproductive structures. The number of stamens varies from zero to several hundred, depending on the species. A stamen consists of a thin filament supporting a thick, knoblike anther. The anther contains pollen sacs which produce pollen, the male gametes. Inside the whorl of stamens are the female reproductive structures, the pistils, or carpels. The pistils have a stigma, a style, and an ovary. The stigma is the sticky part at the top of the pistil. The style is a thin tube that leads from the stigma to the ovary. The ovary is an enlarged area at the base of the pistil that produces ovules which contain the eggs or the female gametes. The number of pistils varies from zero to several dozen, depending on the species. Some flowers have pistils which are fused together. These are called compound pistils. Although the number of stamens and pistils may vary, each flower must have at least one stamen or pistil.

Variation of flowers Flowering plants are either monocotyledons, such as the orchid, or dicotyledons, such as the geranium. Monocotyledons, the smaller of the two groups, usually have flower parts in multiples of three. Dicotyledons usually have flower parts in multiples of four or five. Complete flowers, such as the rose, have all the flower parts, whereas incomplete flowers, such as the pasque flower, are missing one or more of the whorls. A perfect flower, such as the geranium, has both stamens and pistils, while an imperfect flower, such as the cattail, has either stamens or pistils, but not both. A flower with just stamens is male and is called staminate. A flower with just pistils is female and is called pistillate. A dioecious plant, such as the poplar, is either male or female, having either staminate or pistillate flowers, but not both. A monoecious plant, such as corn or oaks, has both staminate and pistillate flowers on the same plant. A polygamous plant, such as buckwheat, has both perfect and imperfect flowers on the same plant.

Flowers have a symmetry which is either radial or bilateral. Radially symmetrical flowers, such as the rose, can be divided in several ways to produce equal sides. Bilaterally symmetrical flowers, such as the snapdragon, have only one way of being divided into two equal sides. Some plants, such as the dandelion, have flowers which grow in clusters at the end of a stalk. This is called inflorescence. Bracts are the leaflike structures under an inflorescence. In composite flowers, such as the daisy, each blossom is actually made up of many tiny flowers called florets. (*See* COMPOSITE FAMILY.) Each floret has its own stamens and pistils, and each one produces its own, separate seed. *See also* CARNIVOROUS PLANT; FERTILIZATION; HYBRID. A.J.C./M.H.S.

Left, the man orchid is so called because of the supposed manlike shape of the flowers.

FLOWMETER (flō′ mēt′ ər) A flowmeter is a device used to measure the flow of substances through a pipe, or other type of conduit. These substances may be liquids, gases, or powders. Some flowmeters measure the quantity of material that flows past a certain point.

The two most common types of flowmeters are rate-of-flow meters, and volumetric meters. Rate-of-flow meters generally contain a small propeller. The propeller is rotated by the flow of liquid through the pipe, and its speed of rotation is measured by an electrical meter. Volumetric flowmeters usually have a drum, or chamber, that has two or three sections. The liquid fills one section at a time and then causes the drum, or chamber, to rotate. The first section is emptied into the pipe while another is being filled. Since the volume of the drum, or chamber, is known, each rotation means that a certain amount of liquid has passed that point.

The flow of gas through pipes is usually measured by a flowmeter that is similar to an anemometer. An anemometer is a device that is used to measure the speed of wind. It consists of small cups mounted on horizontal shafts. The horizontal shafts are attached to a vertical shaft, and rotate around it as wind fills the cups.

Some rate-of-flow meters operate on a pressure difference, which is caused when an obstruction is placed in the path of the flowing material. The pitot tube that is used in airplanes to measure airspeed is one of this type. W.R.P./R.W.L.

FLUID (flü′ əd) A fluid is a substance that is capable of flowing. Any liquid or gas can be a fluid. For example, water at ordinary temperature is a fluid and a liquid. Air is a fluid and a gas. A fluid takes the shape of its container, provided the container is filled. A slight pressure or force changes the form of a fluid. Fluids are also elastic. They tend to return to their former size when the pressure is removed.

A perfect fluid is without friction. In other words, a perfect fluid offers no resistance to flow except that of inertia, or inactivity. A fluid with the same properties or qualities throughout is called a homogeneous fluid.

Usually, pressure changes do not affect the density of an incompressible fluid. An incompressible fluid is one that cannot be pressed together—that is, forced into less space. But in actual practice, no liquid is completely incompressible. An elastic fluid has greater forces resisting changes to size or shape than viscous forces, which resist flow. A viscous fluid, such as molasses, is thick or slow-flowing. This is due to friction. (*See* VISCOSITY.) *See also* FLUIDICS; HYDRAULICS; FLUID MECHANICS. J.J.A./J.T.

FLUIDICS (flü id′ iks) Fluidics is a process that uses a fluid to do jobs normally performed by electronic devices. (*See* ELECTRONICS.) In other words, instead of a stream of electrons flowing along a conductor, a stream of fluid flows along a channel. The fluid can be split or deflected like an electric current. Suitable "circuits," made up of shallow channels carved in plastic, can be built. Fluid circuits can be used as logic devices to build a simple computer. They are slower and bulkier than electronic circuits. But their immunity (resistance) to heat and high radiation levels gives them certain advantages over electronics.

Fluid flow can be switched in direction and amplified by the effect of a control jet. The control jet hits the main flow from one side. Various designs of channels and chambers for the fluids to flow through can produce switching and amplification (increasing) effects like those of electronic devices. Although fluid circuits take only a few thousandths of a second to operate, they are still much slower than electronics.

In the United States, fluid circuits are being used in rocket and aircraft guidance systems. Here the resistance of fluid circuits to vibration is very important. J.J.A./J.T.

FLUID MECHANICS (flü′ əd mi kan′ iks) Fluid mechanics is divided into two branches. Fluid dynamics is the study of how fluids move. It is also known as hydrodynamics. Hydrostatics studies fluids at rest. For example, it studies the pressures within fluids. A fluid is any material that can flow. Both gases and liquids are fluids. There are a number of sciences that study special applications of fluid mechanics. Aeronautics studies the motion of air. It is particularly concerned with the effects of air on flight. Hydraulics studies how the ideas of fluid mechanics can be used for machines. Pneumatics studies compressed air, or air under pressure, and is concerned with how compressed air can be used.

An important part of fluid dynamics is the study of fluids flowing in pipes. Engineers need to know how fast fluids flow in pipes and how this changes in pipes of different widths. The effect of the surface of the pipe on the fluid can also be important. The flow of fluids was first studied by a Swiss mathematician, Daniel Bernoulli. He discovered a mathematical formula for fluid flow by applying the principle of the conservation of energy. The formula connects the pressure and speed of a fluid in different parts of a pipe. The formula is still used today.

Another important discovery was made by a British engineer, Osbourne Reynolds. There are two types of fluid flow, streamlined and turbulent. (*See* STREAMLINING.) In streamlined flow, the flow is steady. In a straight pipe, the molecules in a streamlined fluid move in straight lines. If there is turbu-

The study of fluid mechanics has many practical applications. Some large ships are built with a bulge beneath the bow. Fluid mechanics has shown that this shape improves the flow of water around the hull.

lence, the flow is unsteady. The molecules in a turbulent fluid do not move in straight lines inside a pipe. Reynolds found that whether the flow is streamlined or turbulent depends on its velocity. If the fluid is moving slowly, the flow is streamlined. Then, at a certain velocity, it becomes turbulent. He called this velocity the critical velocity. He discovered how to calculate it. M.E./J.T.

FLUORESCENCE (flùr′ es′ əns) Fluorescence is the light some materials give off when they absorb energy in the form of radiation. The energy excites, or adds energy to, the electrons in the atoms of the substance. The electrons remain excited for about 1/100,000,000 of a second. Then they give off their excess energy as light. The light continues only as long as the energy excites the electrons. Fluorescent materials are much brighter than other materials. The light they give off has more energy than ordinary reflected light.

Fluorescent light can be any color depending upon the substance affected by the energy. A shirt washed with a detergent, or soap powder, containing fluorescent materials, called optical brighteners, gives off a blue-white glow. Sodium vapor gives off yellow light, and neon gives off red light. The arrangement and number of elements in a compound determine the color it gives off.

Many natural substances are fluorescent. Minerals such as fluorite, from which fluorescence takes its name, glow in brilliant colors under ultraviolet light.

Fluorescent substances have many uses. Mercury vapor is a fluorescent substance used in highway lights. Fluorescent screens are used in television picture tubes and electron microscopes. Electric current causes fluorescence in neon signs and fluorescent light bulbs. Paints and inks used in some advertising contain fluorescent substances.

Fluorescence stops as soon as the incoming energy causing it has been removed. Materials that are phosphorescent discharge a light that disappears more slowly than fluorescent light. Some diamonds, for example, glow in the dark for a long time after the lights have been turned off. (*See* PHOSPHORESCENCE.) W.R.P./J.D.

Fluorescent lighting provides an artifical light which is nearer to daylight than the light made by an ordinary filament electric light.

FLUORIDATION (flùr′ ə dā′ shən) Fluoridation is the addition of very small amounts of fluorides to the water supply in order to reduce tooth decay. Sodium fluoride is used most often in fluoridation because it dissolves easily in water.

About one-half of the population of the United States drinks fluoridated water. Many scientists claim that fluoridation helps strengthen the enamel of the tooth, thus decreasing the number of cavities. Those people against fluoridation say that it is unnecessary, and that the long term effects of fluoridation have not been studied yet. *See also* CARIES.

J.M.C./A.D.

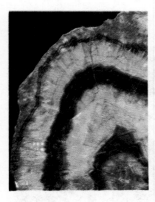

Fluorspar is the mineral source of calcium fluoride. It is widely used in steel making.

FLUORIDE (flùr′ īd′) Fluorides are compounds of fluorine with one other element or group of elements. Most fluorides are salts. They are made by reacting hydrofluoric acid with a metal oxide or hydroxide. Fluorides are very stable compounds. Calcium fluoride occurs in nature as the mineral fluorspar. It is used in steel-making. The mineral cryolite is sodium aluminum fluoride. It is used as a source of aluminum. Hydrogen fluoride is used for etching glass and as a catalyst in the chemical industry. (*See* CATALYST.)

M.E./A.D.

FLUORINE (flùr′ ēn) Fluorine (F) is an element usually found as pale yellow gas. The atomic number of fluorine is 9. Its atomic weight is 18.998. The boiling point of fluorine is −188°C [−306°F]. Its freezing point is −220°C [−364°F]. Fluorine is a member of the halogen group of elements. (*See* HALOGEN.) It was discovered by the French chemist Ferdinand Moissan in 1886. It is an extremely poisonous gas and one of the most reactive of all the elements. It always occurs combined with another element. It is so reactive that it even forms compounds with

noble gases xenon and krypton. Its most common mineral is fluorspar, which is calcium fluoride.

Fluorine is a very difficult gas to handle because it is so reactive. It attacks both glass and metal. Therefore fluorine has few uses, but several of its compounds are widely used. (See COMPOUND.) One very useful group of fluorine compounds are the fluorides. Sodium fluoride in small amounts is used to fluoridate water to fight tooth decay. Another is the fluorocarbons. Fluorocarbons are compounds of fluorine and carbon. Freons are a group of fluorocarbons. They are very unreactive and are used as solvents and in refrigerators. Plastics made from fluorocarbons are tough and resistant to corrosion and chemicals. They are also good insulators against heat and electricity. Fluorocarbon plastics are used for non-stick coatings in cooking utensils and to make artificial joints in surgery. Fluorine also became commercially important during World War II when it was used in producing pure uranium-235. M.E./J.R.W.

FLUX (flǝks) The word flux means ''flow.'' It is used in several different branches of physics. Flux often means the rate at which something flows through a certain area. Flux is used in the study of light. Light is a form of energy. Therefore, a beam of light is a flow of energy. The amount of light energy flowing through a certain area in one second is called the luminous flux. It is measured in lumens in the SI system of units. (*See* INTERNATIONAL SYSTEM.) Nuclear physicists often use beams of subatomic particles. The flux of a beam is the number of particles flowing through a certain area in one second.

Flux is also used in connection with electric and magnetic fields. Fields do not flow. Therefore the flux in these cases is a little different from the examples above. The magnetic flux is the strength of the magnetic field multiplied by the area that it crosses. The

SI unit of magnetic flux is the weber. A capacitor contains two metal plates of the same size, placed very close together. (*See* CAPACITOR AND CAPACITANCE.) If it is connected to a battery, an electric field is set up between the plates. The electric flux between the plates is the electric field multiplied by the area of one plate. This is equal to the charge on the plates. The electric flux is measured in coulombs in the SI system.

Flux has a very different meaning in engineering. Flux is a material added to molten metals when they are being extracted from ores. The flux removes impurities. A flux is used in a similar way when pieces of metal are soldered together. (*See* SOLDERING.) The flux stops metal oxides from forming. If oxides did form, they would not melt at the temperature of the solder. They would remain solid. This would prevent the solder from flowing easily over the metal pieces and weakening the joint. M.E./A.I.

Above, the long-headed fly is a predatory fly, eating other small insects. It lays its eggs in rotting vegetation.

FLY (flī) A fly is any of about 150,000 species of two-winged insects belonging to the order Diptera. Although many small, flying insects are improperly called "flies," only the true flies have two wings instead of four. The true flies include the crane fly, fruit fly, horsefly, housefly, mosquito, and tsetse fly. Many kinds of flies are considered pests because they bite, and some carry diseases such as malaria and typhoid fever. Other flies, though, help with pollination, and others are predators or parasites of harmful insects. Some flies, such as the fruit flies, reproduce so quickly that they are important in genetic research. (*See* GENETICS; HEREDITY.)

Flies range in size from an almost microscopic midge at 1.3 mm [0.05 in] long to the largest, a crane fly at 75 mm [3 in] long. The body of the fly is covered with an exoskeleton and sensitive hairs. (*See* SKELETON.) The head has two large compound eyes, each of which has about 4,000 lenses. (*See* EYE AND VISION.) The mouth parts form a long, hollow proboscis which is used for sucking liquids, the only food of flies. "Biting" flies use the proboscis to stab a victim, inject saliva to prevent the blood from clotting, and suck out the blood. The two antennae vary in size and structure, according to the species. They are used to detect motion and odors in the air.

Flies are the fastest of the flying insects. The buzzing sound they make is due to the beating of their wings. The wings are attached to the thorax. The hind wings have been reduced to form two, short, clublike structures called halteres, which are used for balance in flight. There are six jointed legs with claws or special, sticky pads called pulvilli. The fly breathes through ten pairs of spiracles along its thorax and abdomen.

Most flies reproduce quickly and in large numbers. The female may lay 1 to 250 eggs at a time, depending on the species. These eggs develop into larvae some of which are called maggots. After molting several times, the larva becomes a pupa which will hatch into a fully grown adult. (*See* METAMORPHOSIS.) A.J.C./J.E.R.

FLYING FISH (flī' ing fish') A flying fish is a saltwater fish that belongs to the family Exocoetidae. It has large fins that act in a way similar to wings on its sides. The fish do not actually fly, but they glide through the air. Flying fish swim in schools. Often they are chased by predator fish. To escape, the flying fish swim very fast, break through the water's surface, stretch out their large fins, and glide over the water. By the time they reenter the water, the predators have often become confused and have left. Flying fish feed on plankton. They are found in both the Atlantic and Pacific Oceans.   S.R.G./E.C.M.

An Atlantic flying fish.

FLYING FOX (flī′ ing fäks) The flying fox is a type of bat, so named because of its foxlike face. It is a large bat, measuring about 40 cm [16 in] long, and has about a 1.5 m [5 ft] wingspan. The flying fox belongs to the family Pteropodidae.

Above are flying foxes at rest in a tree.

Flying foxes live mainly on Pacific Ocean islands. They feed at night, usually eating fruit and pollen. Unlike most bats, flying foxes rely on their vision rather than built-in sonar. (*See* BAT.)

Flying foxes spend the day roosting upside down in trees. They may damage the trees when large numbers of them congregate. They also produce problems by stealing fruit from plantations. Because of these qualities, flying foxes may not be brought into the United States.   J.M.C./R.J.B.

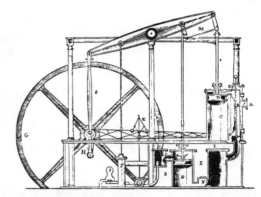

James Watt's condensing steam engine, patented in 1769, used a large flywheel (marked G).

FLYWHEEL (flī′ hwēl′) A flywheel is a device in some kinds of engines which converts bursts of power into a continuous supply of power. An engine is used to produce power. In some engines, the power is produced smoothly, without any interruptions. In other words, it is produced continuously. Steam turbines and jet engines are examples of engines that produce power like this. Other engines do not produce their power continuously. The power is supplied in bursts. Examples include the gasoline engine. In a gasoline engine, a mixture of air and gasoline is exploded inside a cylinder. The explosion pushes the piston along the cylinder and provides the power. The piston moves in bursts and so the power is supplied in bursts. This kind of engine contains a flywheel. A flywheel is a heavy wheel and therefore contains a large amount of inertia. The bursts of power make the flywheel rotate. Its inertia keeps it rotating in between the bursts. (*See* INERTIA.) In this way it converts the power into a smooth continuous supply. M.E./J.T.

FM *See* MODULATION.

FOCUS (fō′ kəs) Focus is the point where light rays meet, or converge, after passing through a convex lens or the curved cornea and lens of the eye.

If the focus is located on the retina of the eye, a clear image is produced. If the focus falls behind or in front of the retina, the image is blurred.

Light rays that strike the center of a curved lens, or the eye, keep their original direction. But rays that strike anywhere else on those surfaces are bent as they pass through. The further away from the center, the more they are bent.

A convex lens, one that curves out, brings parallel rays together to form a real, sharp focus on the side of the lens opposite the object. It forms a real image, which is upside-down and can be focused on a screen. A

virtual image is one that is right side up and on the side of the lens towards the object. A concave lens, one that curves inward, spreads parallel rays apart to form a sharp, virtual focus. A virtual image appears on the same side of the lens as the object as one looks at the object through the lens.

Optical lenses and eyes cannot form sharply focused, undistorted images over a wide field. Nor can they focus on a nearby object and a distant object at the same time. One or the other is blurred. When the eye focuses on a nearby object, the ciliary muscle contracts and increases the curvature and thickness of the lens of the eye. As a result, light rays bend more and focus on the retina. This process is called accommodation.

Heat and sound waves can be brought to a focus in similar ways. A cathode-ray tube

1. A convex lens refracts (bends) light rays so that these converge, or focus, some distance beyond the lens. 2. A concave mirror reflects light rays to a focus. 3. A concave lens refracts light rays so that they diverge and do not come to a focus. A virtual focus can be calculated by projecting the paths of the light rays behind the lens. 4. A virtual focus for a convex mirror can also be calculated.

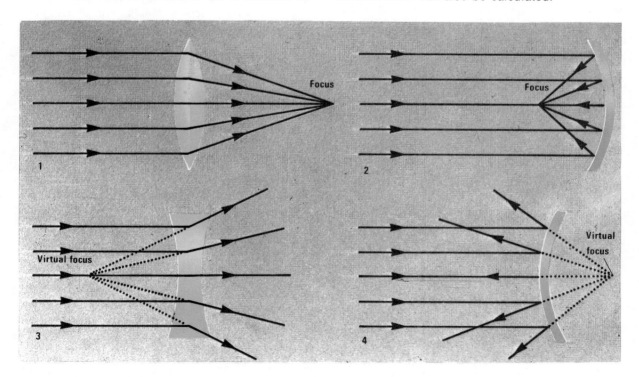

brings a beam of electrons to focus on a phosphorescent screen. *See also* EYE AND VISION; LENS; LIGHT.   W.R.P./S.S.B.

An advection fog is shown above. The fog formed when warm air neared the cold water of the lake.

FOG (fòg) Fog is a cloudlike mass of water droplets which forms on the ground or on the surface of a body of water. There are several different ways that fog forms.

Radiation fog occurs on clear, cool nights if the temperature falls to the dew point. When this happens, the water vapor condenses and forms fog. (*See* CONDENSATION.) Radiation fog is common in valleys.

When warm, moist air blows over colder air, advection fog forms. Advection fog may also form when warm air settles over a cold body of water, or over a snow-covered area. Advection fog is very common in the British Isles.

Frontal fog occurs at a weather front, where two air masses of different temperatures meet. Steam fog occurs when cold air absorbs moisture over a warmer body of water. Steam fog usually only occurs in cold northern climates.

The international definition of fog is a visibility of less than 1 km [1,100 yds]. Many auto accidents occur each year because drivers have trouble seeing through dense fog. Airline departures are often delayed because of fog. Fog is a less serious hazard to ships and aircraft since the invention of radar.
                                                              J.M.C./C.R.

FOLDING (fōld' ing) Folding is a process which produces bends or folds in rock. Fold-

The Himalayas are fold mountains formed from sediments at the bottom of the sea. These sediments were squeezed up into a lofty range when India was forced against the Asian mainland by continental drift.

ing is caused by great compressional (sideways) forces acting on layers of rock in the earth's crust.

Folding is responsible for some of the earth's greatest mountain ranges. There is evidence that the Himalaya mountains in Asia are the result of folding. Scientists believe that India, at one time, was separated from the Asian mainland. Because of continental drift, India eventually rammed into the Asian mainland. (*See* CONTINENTAL DRIFT.) This collision caused a folding up of the sedimentary rock that had accumulated on the sea bed, producing the Himalaya mountains. This theory is supported by the discovery of fossils of sea animals on the upper slopes of Mount Everest, the tallest mountain in the world.

Gentle folding creates a series of symmetrical arches, or upfolds, called anticlines, and downfolds called synclines. (*See* SYMMETRY.)

J.M.C./W.R.S.

FOOD (füd) Food is any substance that provides an organism with nourishment, energy, and the ability to sustain life. Food provides chemical substances, such as vitamins, proteins, carbohydrates, fats, and minerals, which are needed for the building of new cells and tissue.

Organisms obtain food in a variety of ways. Saprophytes obtain food from the dead, rotting remains of other organisms. Parasites obtain food from other living organisms. Plants containing the green pigment chlorophyll manufacture their own food through a series of complex chemical reactions, called photosynthesis. (*See* PHOTOSYNTHESIS.) Photosynthesis is of particular importance because almost all animals depend on photosynthetic plants for food.

Some animals, called herbivores, eat only plants. Other animals, called carnivores, eat only meat. The meat usually comes from herbivores. An omnivore eats both plants and meat. Human beings are omnivores. If plants were to die out, herbivores would lose their source of food and also die out. Once herbivores died out, the carnivores would soon die from starvation. (*See* FOOD CHAIN.)

How people produce food   People produce food in many ways. Agriculture, or farming, developed thousands of years ago. Until about 100 years ago, most farmers in the United States produced only enough food for their own needs. Today, modern equipment and farming methods have greatly increased the American farmer's productivity.

People raise many animals that provide meat and dairy products. Cattle, horses, goats, sheep, and pigs are important food animals in various parts of the world. In the United States, the cow is the major source of dairy products. Chickens provide people with both meat and eggs.

Fishing is an important source of food, especially in areas near the sea. Some countries, like Japan, consume much more fish than meat.

The wealthy, industrialized areas of the world consume the most food. These include the United States, Canada, and Europe. Many countries are able to import food if it cannot be produced at home. For example, Great Britain imports about 75% of its meat, and grows less than half the food its people require.

The people of the poor countries of the world usually eat only what they are able to produce themselves. In some parts of Asia, the people live on rice alone.

How the body uses food   The human body must break down food into simpler substances before the food can be used by the body. It does this through a process called digestion. (*See* DIGESTION.) The digested food travels through the body in the bloodstream. Some of the food provides energy. Some is used to repair or replace cells, and some is stored as fat.

Each person requires a certain amount of food daily, according to size, weight, age,

Facing left, wheat is one of humanity's most important sources of food.

and amount of activity. A person who eats too little loses weight, becomes weak, and may develop poor teeth and vision. A person who overeats becomes stout, and is more likely to develop diseases such as heart disease, and possibly diabetes.

There are several different classes of food. The body digests and uses these types in different ways. Carbohydrates are the major source of energy, and also help in the building up of new cells and tissues. (*See* CARBOHYDRATE.) They are found in sweet and starchy food, like candy, potatoes, and pasta. Fats are a more concentrated form of energy but are more difficult for the body to use. (*See* FAT.) They are plentiful in some meats, butter, nuts, and seeds. Proteins are a very important tissue-building food, and are abundant in meat, eggs, milk, and fish. (*See* PROTEIN.) Other nutrients, like water, vitamins, and minerals, are essential for the proper maintenance of the body. *See also* DIET; METABOLISM.   J.M.C./E.R.L.

FOOD CHAIN (füd chān) A chain is one long object made up of many smaller objects called links. Each link is attached to the next one. The term food chain refers to a situation found in nature. One animal eats another animal. That animal then is eaten by another animal. Each animal is a link in a large "chain" of animals. A common food chain is grass–cow–human. A food chain in the ocean is plankton–snail–small fish–large fish–shark.

All food chains begin with a plant, because it is the only living thing that can make its own food. (*See* PHOTOSYNTHESIS.) Animals must eat other living things to get food.

There are many food chains in an ecosystem. Many of the chains are connected so that they are often called a food web. Although humans are able to eat many things, some animals can eat only one thing. If that one thing is eliminated, the animals will die. This will "break" the food chain and may cause

Food chains are really cycles. Green plants make food from carbon dioxide in the atmosphere, and this food passes in turn to animals, microorganisms such as bacteria, and back again to green plants. Without green plants all other forms of life would die.

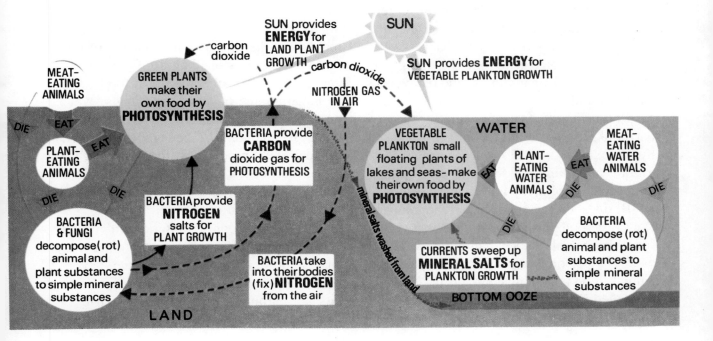

many environmental problems. *See also* ECOLOGY; ENVIRONMENT. S.R.G./R.J.B.

FOOD POISONING (füd′ pòiz′ ning) If a person drinks dirty water, or eats unwashed vegetables, or eats meat that has been left uncovered, that person risks suffering from food poisoning. In air, impure water, and houseflies and other insects, there are always bacteria. Bacteria, and sometimes other microorganisms, can cause illness when they contaminate food. Food contaminated by certain chemicals, such as zinc, lead, and copper, can also cause food poisoning.

Symptoms of food poisoning may include vomiting, cramps, and diarrhea. In some instances, certain muscles may be paralyzed. Food poisoning may be prevented by preparing and storing foods properly. Sanitary methods are very important in preparing and storing food. With care, many types of food poisoning could be avoided.

Food spoiled by bacteria usually has an unpleasant taste and smell. Such foods are generally avoided. Sometimes bacteria in food produce dangerous—even deadly—substances without causing much change in flavor. These substances are the toxins (poisons) that cause food poisoning. Often, bacteria called Salmonellae cause food poisoning. Staphylococcus probably causes the most common type of food poisoning. It is mild in comparison to others, and recovery is usually rapid.

Botulism is a far more serious type of bacterial food poisoning. Botulism is caused by the toxins produced by the bacterium *Clostridium botulinum*. In some cases, botulism may cause respiratory failure and death.

Besides bacteria, other microorganisms can cause food poisoning. But these are often found in animals rather than humans. However, if a person eats the flesh of a poisoned animal, food poisoning could occur. Turkeys have died in great numbers after eating food contaminated by a fungus called *Aspergillus*.

Some species of this fungus produce aflatoxins. These are poisons and also carcinogens. Carcinogens are substances which can cause cancer.

People can poison their own food, and that of animals, by careless use of herbicides and pesticides. Some of these chemicals are very poisonous. If food, such as grain and fruit, is heavily treated with such chemicals—and the food is not washed before being eaten—poisoning can follow. (*See* POLLUTION.) *See also* FOOD PRESERVATION.

J.J.A./J.J.F.

FOOD PRESERVATION

Food preservation (füd′ prez ər vā′ shən) is the science of treating food so that it will keep, over a period of time, its flavor, color, texture, and nutrients. Food preservation also involves treating food so that it will not spoil or be contaminated by harmful bacteria. Foods spoil because of chemical changes and because of the growth of tiny forms of life called microorganisms. Microorganisms, such as bacteria, yeasts, and molds, are the most common causes of food decay. They grow in all kinds of food. Molds change the flavor of some moist foods, such as bread. Some bacteria form acids, which turn food sour. Yeast may ferment food, or make it alcoholic. (*See* FERMENTATION.) Some bacteria produce hydrogen sulfide. Hydrogen sulfide is a gas that may, in combining with iron in food, turn food black and give it the odor of rotten eggs.

Chemical spoilage of foods often takes place during storage. Stored foods may change or develop bad odors and flavors. Chemical changes occur in their proteins, fats, and carbohydrates. When exposed to air, fats and oils oxidize (combine with oxygen).

When this happens with butter, butter is described as having turned rancid, or having developed an "old" taste. (*See* OXIDATION.)

Many foods spoil because of attack by their own enzymes. All living things produce enzymes. These substances are important in digestion. Enzyme activity also causes fruits to ripen and meats to become tender. However, if not checked, enzyme activity can result in decay. It can also cause a loss of nutrients, such as vitamin C. Food exposed to the air is also subject to attack from insects. Insects not only carry germs. They may lay their eggs on the food.

Methods of food preservation   Many new processes of food preservation have been developed through science and technology. All methods of food preservation must be performed under clean conditions, using only products at the proper stage of ripeness. Spoiled food parts must be discarded. Parts that are not to be eaten must be removed.

There are eight basic methods of food preservation. Canning involves sterilizing food, or making it free of germs. Canning also involves keeping air away from food. Heating food to high temperatures destroys microorganisms. It also stops enzyme activity. Most germ-killing temperatures range from 100°C to 121°C [212°F to 250°F]. Meat, fish, and most vegetables are heated to about 120°C [248°F]. The sterilizing time depends on the temperature, the container, and the type of food.

Fresh peas are being prepared for canning.

Cans are being run through a sterilizer.

Canners pack food in airtight metal or glass containers. To achieve this, air is removed from the containers and the containers are then sealed with airtight lids. This keeps air away from food and also keeps out microorganisms. Most canned foods keep for more than a year.

Cold storage keeps food fresh at low temperatures. Cold storage temperatures, ranging from $-1°C$ to $10°C$ [30°F to 50°F] do not stop spoilage. But they do slow microorganism growth and enzyme action. The cold storage life of foods depends on the type of food, the storage temperature, and the amount of moisture in the air of the storage room. Keeping the air in motion around cold-storage food helps maintain a constant temperature. It also removes gases that some foods give off. Some of these gases lessen the storage life of fruit. Meat processors use cold storage to tenderize meat. They put meat in cold rooms for a week to ten days. The cold prevents spoilage by microorganisms. The cold also allows a slow enzyme action. This action aids in breaking down the tougher tissues, therefore making the meat more tender.

Freezing is second to canning as one of the most widely used methods of food preservation. Freezing is an effective way of preserving foods, since microorganisms cannot grow at low temperatures. Also, enzyme action is slowed down a great deal. In 1929, the American inventor Clarence Birdseye developed a quick-freezing process. This process cools food quickly to $-35°C$ [$-31°F$]. During slow-freezing, the water inside the cells of food has time to freeze and grow into large ice crystals. These break up the cells, releasing enzymes. In quick-freezing, the water forms smaller ice crystals, which have little effect on the cell structure. On thawing a slow-frozen product, water drains from the broken cell, carrying the nutrients with it. It then spoils very quickly because of the release of enzymes. A quick-frozen food has its cells intact and does not lose nutrients or flavor. Commercial food processors freeze most kinds of fruits, vegetables, and some kinds of meat, fish, poultry, and dairy products. Food companies also freeze a variety of pre-cooked foods ranging from French fried potatoes to complete dinners.

Drying, also called dehydration, removes most of the moisture from food. Microorganisms cannot grow on dry food. Enzyme action cannot take place in the absence of moisture. Drying also reduces the size and weight of foods. This makes foods easier to transport and store. Food processors often blanch vegetables and fruits before drying to prevent changes caused by enzymes. In blanching, the foods are exposed to steam or boiling water. Processors often treat apples, pears, and other fruit with sulfur dioxide gas. This prevents enzyme and other chemical changes. Sun-drying is the oldest method of drying food. Processors spread the food on trays and expose it to the air. Kiln-drying uses heat from a furnace or stove to evaporate moisture from food. Dehydrators use a vacuum to make water evaporate at a low temperature. Dehydrators take less time than the other means of drying to process the same amount of food. In spray-drying, liquid food is sprayed through nozzles into specially designed drying chambers. Food particles collect at the bottoms of the chambers as powder.

In the process of quick-freezing (above) raspberries are passed through a stream of vaporized liquid nitrogen. This preserves them intact.

The cans above are being automatically filled with peas.

Freeze-drying removes water from food while the food is still frozen. The frozen food is cooled to about −29°C [−20°F]. Then it is placed on a tray in a vacuum chamber or room. Heat is then applied. In this method, the frozen water in the food is evaporated without melting. Freeze-dried foods are usually packed in an inert gas such as nitrogen.

Curing is a method of preserving foods that has been used for many years. Curing consists of salting, smoking, cooking, and drying, or some combination of these treatments. In some kinds of curing, other chemicals besides salt are used. The most widely used ones (other than salt) are sugar, vinegar, and wood smoke. Some other chemicals include potassium and sodium nitrite, sulfur dioxide, and benzoic acid. The United States Department of Agriculture limits the amount of sodium nitrite used in curing. Under certain conditions, sodium nitrite can combine with other chemicals to form compounds that may cause cancer. Salt is used in large amounts to control microorganism growth. Because salt

has a strong taste, processors use large amounts only in foods where it adds to the flavor, such as beef and pork. Sugar in large amounts helps preserve foods such as jams, jellies, and frozen fruits. Sugar also improves the flavor of these foods. Vinegar is used to pickle many foods, such as cucumbers, onions, herring, and sardines. Vinegar gives such foods a sour taste, but one that many people like. The acetic acid in vinegar slows microorganism growth. Wood smoke contains chemicals that slow the growth of microorganisms. Smoking also changes the odor and flavor of food. Smoking preserves meat and fish well, if combined with salting and drying.

Sardines in Portugal are dried by laying them out on racks in the hot sun.

Doctors use antibiotics to destroy microorganisms that make people ill. Scientists found that they can also be used to stop microorganisms that spoil food. In Canada, food processors dip fish into a weak solution of certain antibiotics, such as Aureomycin and Terramycin. This slows the growth of microorganisms. It also extends the time fish can be kept in refrigerated storage.

Ultraviolet rays can destroy microorganisms, but they are not commonly used in preserving food. Ultraviolet rays are used to kill spores in the air in bakeries, control mold in packaged cheese, and reduce bacterial damage in meat. (*See* IRRADIATION; ULTRAVIOLET LIGHT.)

Food preservation has totally changed our eating habits. Because people can preserve food, they can enjoy healthy diets all year long. In one meal, a person may eat refrigerated salmon from Alaska, quick frozen corn from Iowa, and canned pineapple from Hawaii.

Many people enjoy canning or quick-freezing foods in their homes. But most preserved foods are prepared by the food-processing industry. In the United States alone, more than 1,500,000 persons are employed by this industry. *See also* FOOD; FOOD POISONING. J.J.A./F.W.S.

FOOTCANDLE (fut′ kan′ dəl) A footcandle is a unit of illumination or illuminance. Illumination is the amount of light falling on an area of surface. One footcandle is equivalent to the illumination produced by a source with an intensity of one candle at a distance of one foot.

An illumination of 10 to 20 footcandles may be enough for ordinary book-reading purposes. As many as 50 footcandles may be required by a draftsman. The sunlight at noon gives an illumination of 5,000 to 10,000 footcandles. J.J.A./S.S.B.

FOOT-POUND (fut paund) Foot-pound is the unit used to measure energy and work. Energy is the ability to do work. Work is the overcoming of resistance. Scientists define work as the action of force through distance. A force must be exerted to overcome a resistance, such as weight. When the force is exerted through a distance, work is done.

For example, when a one-pound weight is lifted straight up a distance of one foot, one foot-pound of work is done. When a force of one foot-pound is exerted in order to move a weight of one pound along a horizontal surface, one foot-pound of work is done for every foot the object is moved. If a machine is capable of doing 33,000 foot-pounds of work in one minute, it is said to have a rating of one horsepower.

In the metric system, energy and work are measured in joules, or in kilogram-meters. One foot-pound equals 1.356 joules. *See also* FOOT-POUND-SECOND-SYSTEM. W.R.P./R.W.L.

FOOT-POUND-SECOND SYSTEM	
FPS units	**Metric system**
1 inch	2.54 centimeters
1 foot	30.48 centimeters
1 yard	91.44 centimeters
1 mile	1.61 kilometers
1 ounce	28.35 grams
1 pound	453.59 grams
1 ton	907.18 kilograms
1 gallon	3.78 liters
1 British thermal unit	1,055.06 joules

FOOT-POUND-SECOND SYSTEM (fut′ paund′ sek′ ənd sis′ təm) The foot-pound-second system is a system of units used for measuring. It was first used in England hundreds of years ago. The units are based on simple quantities. The foot is based on the length of a human foot. One of the units of weight is the stone. This was based on the weight of a certain stone. The foot-pound-second system is often abbreviated to the FPS system. Its units were not developed for scientific use. They are difficult to use in calculations. The relationships between the units are

not systematic. For example, 12 inches is 1 foot, 3 feet is 1 yard, 22 yards is 1 chain, 10 chains is 1 furlong, 8 furlongs is 1 mile. Because of this difficulty, the FPS system is no longer used in science. The SI system is usually used instead. (*See* INTERNATIONAL SYSTEM.) The SI system is based on the meter, the kilogram, and the second, and is much easier to use. Some FPS units are still used in America. The FPS system uses the Fahrenheit scale of temperature. On this scale, water boils at 212°F and freezes at 32°F. The SI system uses the Celsius scale.   M.E./R.W.L.

FORAMINIFERIDA (fə ram′ ə nif′ ə ri də) Foraminiferida is an order of tiny organisms of the phylum Protozoa. They move about by means of a pseudopodia, or "fake foot." Foraminiferans live in both fresh and salt water, and are found at all depths. They feed on microscopic organisms.

Foraminiferans have shells made of horny, chalky, or glassy material. When they die, their shells sink and become part of the foraminiferal ooze, which covers about 30% of the ocean floor.

Foraminiferans reproduce sexually and asexually. (*See* REPRODUCTION.) The parent usually dies during reproduction because it loses most of its cytoplasm. *See also* CELL.
                    J.M.C./R.J.B.

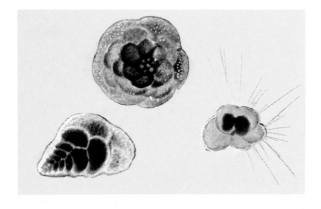

Foraminiferida are single-celled organisms with shells having one or more chambers.

FORCE (fōrs) A force, in physics, is an influence that causes a change in the movement or shape of a body. A change in movement may be from standing still to moving, or it may be from moving at one speed to moving faster (acceleration), or it may be from moving in one direction to moving in another. The study of forces and how they affect bodies is called mechanics.

Forces need not produce an apparent change. A book lying on a table is being pulled by the force of gravity, which keeps it lying on the table. It doesn't fall because the table exerts a counterforce against it. (*See* DYNAMICS.)

Forces can change the shape of a body. When a rubber ball hits the ground, it becomes squashed for a moment. But then elastic forces in the ball cause it to return to its original shape. (*See* ELASTICITY.)

A force always has a particular strength and always acts in a particular direction. The strength of a force is usually measured in units called newtons. The amount of acceleration produced by a force depends on the mass of the body. The larger the mass, the less the acceleration. The strength of a force can be calculated by letting it accelerate a body. The acceleration of the body and its mass can both be measured. From these quantities, the strength of the force can be calculated.

Scientists now recognize four fundamental forces that act upon all matter. This includes bodies of matter we can see, as well as tiny, subatomic particles invisible to the human eye. Two of these forces, gravity and electromagnetism, produce effects that we are familiar with. But the other two act upon something we can never see — the nucleus of an atom. The force that holds the nuclei together is called the strong force. The other, called the weak force, causes a slow process of nuclear change, such as beta decay, or the emission of electrons. (*See* RADIOACTIVITY.)
                    M.E./A.I.

Henry Ford drives his first automobile, which he built in 1896. The car was powered by a two-cylinder, four horsepower engine.

FORD, HENRY (1863–1947) Henry Ford (fōrd) was an American manufacturer and inventor who developed the first mass-produced automobile. Ford began producing his Model T auto in 1908. He used moving assembly line methods which were completely new to the industry. These assembly line methods allowed Ford to offer more cars to the American public at a lower price than anyone before him. Between 1908 and 1927 Ford's company, the Ford Motor Company, built and sold over 15 million Model Ts. That was more than half of all the cars sold in the United States during that period.

In Ford's moving assembly line, the main parts of a car were put together as the car moved along on a slow-moving conveyor system. The workers stayed in one place, and performed their special jobs as the cars passed their station. It took about 93 minutes to put a car together with this system. Ford's assembly line methods revolutionized American industry. Today, many products are built on assembly lines.

In the early 1900s, only well-to-do persons could afford to own an automobile.

Ford, however, believed that every man should be able to own a car. He made only a small profit on each Model T that was sold. But he sold so many that the company was able to grow and prosper.

Ford also shocked his fellow manufacturers with another theory. He believed that it was important for manufacturers to pay their employees high wages. The average skilled worker at that time was receiving $2.50 a day. Ford raised the salaries of his skilled workers to $5.00 a day, and shortened their work day from nine hours to eight hours. Later, he raised the minimum for skilled workers to $6.00. Ford felt that the higher wages would allow his workers to purchase the cars they were building. That is exactly what happened. Ford sales went up dramatically as the thousands of Ford Company workers began to purchase cars.

In 1932, Ford introduced a powerful V-8 (8-cylinder) engine. Up to that time, most automobiles contained 6-cylinder engines. The V-8 engine was soon adopted by other manufacturers. Today, 4-cylinder engines are widely used in autos.

Ford made millions of dollars, and looked for ways of helping others. He contributed heavily to many charitable causes. Ford restored the historical Wayside Inn at Sudbury, Massachusetts, and operated it as a tavern and museum. He established Greenfield Village, a group of historical landmarks and buildings, in Dearborn, Michigan, his hometown. The Ford Museum, also known as the Edison Institute, covers over 200 acres in Dearborn. A large part of Ford's fortune went towards creating the Ford Foundation. The Ford Foundation is the world's largest philanthropic organization. It gives money for scholarships, and aids economic growth in underdeveloped countries. The Foundation also provides money for special studies on mental health, teacher's salaries, and other important matters.

Ford's grandson, Henry Ford II, became

president of the Ford Motor Company in 1945, two years before his grandfather's death. Henry Ford II continued many of his grandfather's policies, and the company is still one of the leaders in the field. Henry Ford II remained active in company affairs until 1979.   W.R.P./D.G.F.

FORENSIC SCIENCE (fə ren' sik sī' əns)

Forensic science is the application of science and technology to questions of civil and criminal law. It is not a branch of science, but a particular way of using many branches of science, including medicine, biology, chemistry, photography, and ballistics. Forensic scientists work with the police and other investigative agencies to help establish how and when a particular crime was committed. They analyze evidence found at the scene of the crime. Often, their scientific work leads to the capture of the criminal.

Forensic medicine is one of the best-known aspects of forensic science. It is particularly important in the case of violent death or injury. When a person is suspected of having died from unnatural causes, a doctor examines the body in detail. The doctor must decide how long the person has been dead. One way the doctor does this is by measuring the temperature of the body. He or she also notes the temperature of the surroundings, and the amount of clothing on the body. A doctor knows that a dead body cools at a certain rate under normal conditions. From these measurements, he or she therefore can determine the approximate time of death. More complicated methods are used when the body has been dead for a long period of time.

Forensic doctors must also determine the actual cause of death. If the victim died of a stab wound, doctors must be able to figure out the size and shape of the weapon. Also, they must determine if it was made by a knife, hatchet, or blunt instrument. In the case of gunshot wounds, doctors work with ballistic experts to determine the caliber, or size, of the

"Dusting" objects with a special powder can make fingerprints on the object visible.

bullet. They also must be able to tell the angle of penetration in the body, and the distance from which the shot was fired. The bullet, or bullets, are examined under a microscope for signs that tell what type of gun was used. Most guns leave individual marks on the bullets they fire.

Many techniques of chemical analysis are used by forensic scientists. Tiny fragments of paint embedded in a victim's skin can lead to exact information about the year, model, and make of the car that struck the person. Forensic scientists analyze paper and ink, for example, in cases of forgery. Almost invisible trademarks, called watermarks, on most paper can lead scientists and detectives to determine where and when the paper was purchased. Ink can be analyzed and traced to its source of supply.

Bloodstains on clothing and other objects at the scene of the crime are analyzed. Forensic scientists can determine the blood group. A tiny bit of dust found in a victim's shirt pocket, or a bit of mud clinging to a shoe can lead to important information about where the crime took place.

Fingerprints are an important part of forensic science. Criminals sometimes leave their fingerprints on objects, such as doorknobs and drinking glasses, at the scene of the crime. Fingerprint experts sprinkle a fine, white powder on these objects, and the fingerprints appear. Every person has individual fingerprint patterns, and everyone who is arrested by the police has his or her fingerprints recorded. The fingerprint experts check the prints they find at the scene of the crime against the files of fingerprints kept at the police station. In this way, they can often determine the identity of the criminal. The largest file of fingerprint records is kept in Washington, D.C. by the Federal Bureau of Investigation (FBI). Local police can also check with the FBI fingerprint files when they are seeking to identify somebody.

Photography is another method that is used in criminal and civil investigations. A camera can often capture details that are not readily visible to the unaided eye. Forensic scientists also make use of infrared or ultraviolet light and X rays to examine evidence. W.R.P./R.W.L.

FORESTRY (fôr′ ə strē) Forestry is the practice of managing forests. There are many different ways to manage a forest. Paper and wood companies own huge forests, cut down the trees, and grow new ones to make products from them. They manage forests so that they produce the largest possible number of desired trees in the shortest time. (*See* LUMBER.) Other forests are wildlife refuges (places for animals to live), recreational areas (such as national parks), or places to fight soil erosion (conservation districts).

A forester uses a mechanical bush cutter to clear away undergrowth from young trees.

Foresters do many things. They chop down trees, plant new trees, fight forest fires, prevent plant diseases, and study the best ways to use a forest. Many foresters are ecologists so that they can understand more about forests. (*See* ECOLOGY.)

Forests are valuable natural resources. Since they grow back after they are used, they are a renewable resource. We need wood and wood products but we must be careful not to cut down all the trees in a forest. This can lead to serious environmental problems such as erosion, flooding, and extermination of animals. *See also* CONSERVATION; ENVIRONMENT; TREE. S.R.G./R.J.B.

FORGING (fōr′ jing) Forging is a means of shaping metal by heating it, then hammering or pressing it into the desired form. When a metal is forged, it loses its grainy structure. It becomes fiberlike. The fiberlike structure gives more strength to the forged object.

One of the oldest forms of forging was carried out by blacksmiths in making horseshoes. They heated iron bars in a fire. They made the fire burn fiercely by blowing air through it with bellows. Gripping a red-hot bar with tongs, they placed it on a heavy anvil and beat it into shape with a heavy hammer.

Most forging operations today are performed with mechanical hammers. A single forging hammer may weigh more than 450,000 kg [1,000,000 lb]. A single forged piece, called a forging, can weigh more than 91,000 kg [200,000 lb]. Tools called dies do the shaping. One die fits on top of the metal. Another die fits on the bottom. When the dies are pressed or hammered together, they squeeze the hot metal into the required shape.

Smith forgings, also called flat-die forgings, are made on machines known as double-frame hammers. In such machines, the lower die is held still. The upper die, driven by steam power, moves up and down in a series of blows.

In drop-hammer forging, also called impact-die forging, the hot metal is forced into shapes that are cut into the upper and lower dies. In the same way as Smith forging, the upper die, powered by steam or electricity, moves up and down repeatedly. A drop hammer can produce objects much faster than Smith forging. Drop-hammer forging also produces shapes that Smith forging cannot produce.

Above, a hammer and anvil.

Press forging is carried out by a squeezing action, as opposed to a series of blows. The dies are similar to the ones used for drop-hammer forging. The dies are squeezed together by either mechanical or hydraulic pressure.

Upset forging is involved with operations such as making heads on nails or bolts. Unlike the other types of forging, upset forging is performed horizontally. *See also* HY-DRAULICS.   J.J.A./J.T.

A section of intestine preserved in formalin, a solution of formaldehyde.

The methods of forging have been used for a long time. Above, a steam hammer used for forging steel in 1861.

FORMALDEHYDE (fȯr mal′ də hīd′) Formaldehyde (HCH═O) is a colorless gas with an irritating odor. Its boiling point is −21°C [−6°F]. It is used in industry to produce a number of artificial resins. These resins are used as varnishes and coatings for electrical insulators. (*See* RESIN.) Formaldehyde is the first member of a group of organic compounds called aldehydes. Formaldehyde is soluble in water. A solution of formaldehyde is called formalin. Formalin is widely used in biology and medical studies to preserve specimens. It is also a useful disinfectant.   M.E./J.M.

FORSYTHIA (fər sith′ ē ə) Forsythia is a genus of seven deciduous shrubs belonging to the olive family. It may grow as tall as 2.7 m [9 ft] with spreading branches. The bell-shaped flowers are bright yellow, giving rise to the nickname, golden bell. The flowers grow in clusters and bloom in the spring before the leaves open. Forsythia is native to China, but is now cultivated throughout the world. Since forsythia is a hardy plant that grows well in a variety of soils, it is a popular garden plant and is used by many states as a decorative ground cover along highways.

A.J.C./M.H.S.

FOSSIL

Fossils (fäs′ əls) are the remains of ancient plants and animals. They have been preserved in various ways, sometimes for hundreds of millions of years.

Animal fossils usually consist only of teeth, shell, or bone fragments, although occasionally an animal fossil is discovered intact. Often, the outline of a plant or animal is embedded in sedimentary rock. Rocks containing fossils often originated beneath the sea, but have been lifted by earth movements to form mountain ranges and new land areas. Erosion then wears away the rock, sometimes enough to expose the fossil.

Fossil formation An important condition of fossil formation is the rapid burial of the dead plant or animal. If the dead organism is exposed to the weather, it will quickly decompose. But if the dead organism is quickly covered by sediment, it has a much better chance of preservation.

Another important factor in plant and animal fossilization is the presence of hard parts of the animal's body. Bones, teeth, and shells in animals, and woody tissue in plants are the most common remains that are preserved. (*See* WOODY PLANT.)

Very few creatures have been preserved in their original state. An exception is the woolly mammoth, some of which have been discovered intact in Alaska and Siberia. They were so well preserved in ice that their meat was still fresh.

Fossils of complete skeletons are relatively common. In California prehistoric animals were trapped when they sank into tar pits. Their skeletons were preserved, but their flesh decomposed.

Fossils that have partially or completely turned to stone are called petrified fossils.

1. Cone-bearing cycads first grew during the Permian period. They still grow today. 2. Leaf fossils are often found as black outlines in rocks. 3. A fossil cast of tree bark.

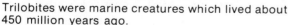

Trilobites were marine creatures which lived about 450 million years ago.

Sometimes, ground water dissolves the remains of a plant or animal. Minerals then replace the remains. This process of petrification is called replacement, and often leaves a perfect replica of the original organism.

Another method of petrification is called permineralization. This occurs when minerals fill in air spaces in the bones or in other hard parts of the fossil without changing its original shape. The minerals actually strengthen the fossil. The Petrified Forest National Monument in Arizona has thousands of petrified logs, in which every molecule of woody tissue has been replaced by stone. (*See* PETRIFIED FOREST.)

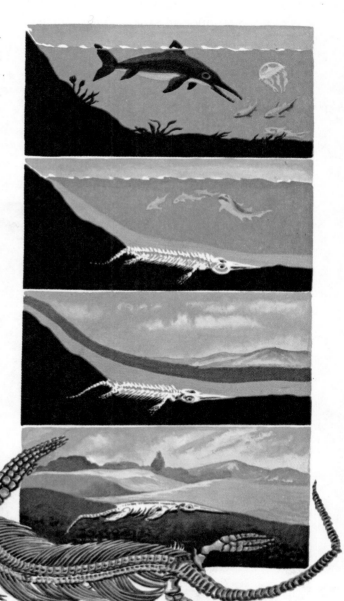

The fossilization of an ichthyosaur. The animal dies and its body sinks into mud at the bottom of the sea. The flesh and bones decay, leaving a fossil cast. The layers of mud and sand which cover the fossil thicken and are turned into rock. The bed of the sea is raised during an upheaval of the earth's crust and becomes land. The land is eroded by wind and rain and eventually the fossil appears.

Fossils of plant leaves and soft-bodied animals are often formed by a process called carbonization. In carbonization, an organism, like a jellyfish, may decompose after a rapid burial until all that remains is a thin film of carbon smeared on rock. This film often shows much detail of the original organism.

Sometimes, a buried organism is completely dissolved, leaving a space in the rock. This space, called a mold, corresponds to the original shape of the organism. Paleontologists (scientists who study fossils) can fill this mold to produce an exact replica, or cast, of the original organism.

Some insects and other small organisms have been preserved by sap. The sap from a tree traps the organism, and then hardens into an amber shell. The entire organism is often preserved.

Footprints, animal droppings, and eggs have also been preserved as fossils. Paleon-tologists believe that dinosaur footprints made in mud were baked hard by the sun before being covered by sediment. Footprints have been found that were covered for millions of years. By studying them, scientists estimate the size and weight of the creatures that made them.

The importance of fossils   Until recently, people believed that the earth had only existed for a few thousand years. Fossils were thought to be the remains of animals killed during the great flood told of in the Bible.

Today, fossils provide an important link to the past history of the earth. Scientists can study the progress of evolution by finding the age of fossils, using methods of dating. A better understanding of the climate and other conditions of the primitive earth has been obtained from fossils. Fossils may also pro-

The fossil cast of a plesiosaur.

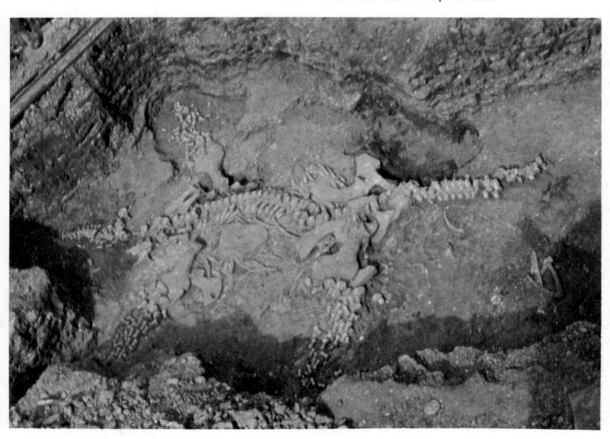

vide clues to the geologist in locating coal and oil deposits, as well as valuable ore-bearing rocks. The earliest known fossils, which are of algae, are about 3.5 billion years old. *See also* EARTH; GEOLOGICAL TIME SCALE.

J.M.C./W.R.S.

A plaster cast of a mammoth found preserved in ice in the Soviet Union.

Many petrified tree trunks are found in the Petrified Forest National Park, Arizona. These trees grew about 200 million years ago.

FOUCAULT, JEAN (1819–1868) Jean Foucault (fü′ kō′) was a French physicist. He made important discoveries about light and about electricity. In 1851, he found a way to demonstrate the rotation of the earth. He did this using a heavy pendulum swinging on a very long wire. (*See* FOUCAULT PENDULUM.) Soon after this he studied the way a gyroscope is affected by the earth's rotation. The modern ship's gyro-compass has been developed from Foucault's discoveries.

In 1855, Foucault discovered the eddy currents that caused early dynamos to overheat. (*See* INDUCTION.) Foucault also found out that light travels at different speeds in water and in air. (*See* REFRACTION OF LIGHT.)

C.M./D.G.F.

FOUCAULT PENDULUM (fü′ ko′ pen′ jə ləm) The Foucault pendulum was built by a French physicist named Jean Foucault in 1851. Using the pendulum, Foucault was

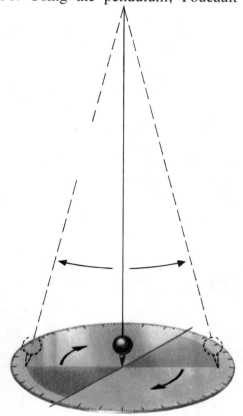

Above, Foucault's pendulum.

able to demonstrate that the earth rotates on its axis. He hung a heavy ball on the end of a steel wire 60 m [66 yd] long. He then made it swing back and forth in a straight line. Very slowly the direction of this line turned round. This effect was not caused by gravity. Gravity only acts in a vertical direction. It could not cause the line of the pendulum to move. The effect was caused by the rotation of the earth. Mathematicians have calculated how big the effect should be. Their results agree with the experiment. The rate at which the plane of the pendulum moves varies. At the poles of the earth it takes 24 hours to make a complete revolution. Nearer to the equator, the time becomes longer. At the equator itself, the plane of the pendulum does not move at all.   M.E./J.T.

FOX (fäks) The fox is a carnivorous (meat-eating) mammal of the dog family Canidae. It has a pointed snout and big bushy tail, and is usually about 1.2 m [4 ft] long, and about 0.3 m [1 ft] high. A female fox is called a vixen.

Foxes have a variety of colors, ranging from brown to red to silver. They live throughout the northern hemisphere. There is one species, the fennec, which lives in the Sahara desert in Africa.

Foxes hunt at night, being aided by their keen senses of sight, smell, and hearing. They feed mainly on rodents and various small animals, but will occasionally eat poultry.

Foxes usually live in burrows which they dig themselves, but occasionally they find a home in a hole in a tree.   J.M.C./R.J.B.

FOXGLOVE (fäks′ glǝv′) The foxglove is any of about 30 species of biennial plants belonging to the genus *Digitalis,* native to Europe. This herbaceous plant grows as tall as 1.5 m [5 ft] and produces a spike of bell-shaped flowers, each of which is about 6 cm [2.4 in] long. The color of the flower varies from purple to pink to white, depending on the species. *Digitalis purpurea* has purple blossoms with spotted interiors. The large, oval, greenish gray leaves of this species contain digitalin, an alkaloid which is poisonous.

The flowers of a hybrid foxglove plant.

These foxes have ears adapted to the climate in which they live. Left, a common fox with average-sized ears. Middle, the fennec, a fox that lives in deserts, whose large ears lose heat and help to keep it cool. Right, an Arctic fox, with small ears that radiate away very little heat from its body.

Digitalin can be used in small amounts, however, to treat patients with certain heart diseases.
A.J.C./M.H.S.

FRACTION (frak′ shən) Fraction means a part of something. The word comes from the Latin word *fractum,* meaning "a breaking." In their simplest forms, fractions are parts of a whole. If a whole is divided into two equal parts, the parts are called halves. Three equal parts are thirds, four are fourths, five are fifths, six are sixths, and so on. In arithmetic, one-half is written as ½. One-third is written ⅓, one-fourth ¼, one-fifth $^1/_5$, one-sixth $^1/_6$, and so on.

In mathematics, a fraction shows one number divided by another. The top number is divided by the bottom number. ¾ means 3 ÷ 4. The top figure, in this case the 3, is called the numerator. The bottom figure, the 4, is called the denominator. A fraction having 1 as the numerator is called a unit fraction.

If the numerator is greater than the denominator, the fraction is greater than one. For example, five-fourths, written as $^5/_4$, is greater than one, or $^4/_4$. The fraction $^5/_4$ can also be written as 1¼, which is one and one-fourth. Fractions greater than one are called improper fractions. Fractions less than one are called proper fractions. All fractions mentioned so far are called common fractions, or simple fractions. A common fraction is a fraction whose numerator and denominator are both integers. Integers are whole numbers, such as 1, 2, 3, and so on, including 0. A complex fraction is a fraction having another fraction in the numerator, or denominator, or both. Examples:

$$\frac{\frac{1}{3}}{7} \qquad \frac{7}{\frac{1}{3}} \qquad \frac{\frac{1}{3}}{\frac{1}{7}}$$

Fractions with denominators such as 10, 100, 1000, and so on are called decimal fractions. Decimal fractions are most often written simply as the numerator, but with a period, or point, at the front. For example, $^8/_{10}$ is written as .8 or 0.8, and $1^8/_{10}$ is written 1.8. Also, $^8/_{100}$ is written .08, $^8/_{1000}$ as .008, and so on. Fractions can be converted to decimals by dividing the bottom number (denominator) into the top number (numerator). For example, ¾ = 3 ÷ 4 = 0.75. *See also* ALGEBRA; ARITHMETIC.
J.J.A./S.P.A.

FRACTURE (frak′ chər) A fracture is a break in a bone. There are several types of fractures. A simple fracture is a clean break of a bone. In a compound fracture, the broken bone sticks out through the skin. A comminuted fracture is a bone that has splintered or shattered. An impacted fracture involves the ends of two bones rubbing against each other. A greenstick fracture is a partial break of a bone.

A fracture causes pain and inflammation in the area around it. Older people with brittle bones are most apt to get a fracture. Children tend to resist fracture.

Bone fractures: 1. A simple fracture. 2. A compound fracture. 3. A comminuted fracture. 4. An impacted fracture. 5. A greenstick fracture.

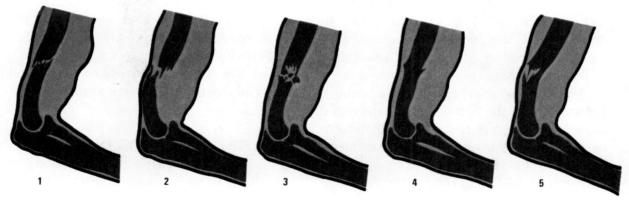

1   2   3   4   5

Usually, when a fracture occurs, a doctor must set the bone so it heals properly. A plaster cast is often applied to the limb with the fracture. The healing of a fracture may take several months.   J.M.C./J.J.F.

FRANCIUM (fran′sē əm) Francium (Fr) is a radioactive metallic element. The atomic number of francium is 87. Its melting point is 27°C [81°F]. It boils at 667°C [1,233°F]. The relative density of francium is not yet known. It only occurs in very small quantities in the earth since it decays very quickly to form other elements. It is formed in the earth by the radioactive decay of heavier elements. It is also formed by artificial means. It was discovered by the French chemist Marguerite Perey in 1939. She named it after her own country. The longest-lived isotope of francium is francium-223. This isotope decays by half in only 22 minutes. (*See* ISOTOPE.) *See also* RADIOACTIVITY.   M.E./J.R.W.

Benjamin Franklin

FRANKLIN, BENJAMIN (1706–1790) Benjamin Franklin (frangk′ lin) was a famous American statesman, philosopher, printer, and journalist. In 1776, Franklin helped to draw up the Declaration of Independence. In 1787, he helped to draw up the Constitution of the United States.

Franklin also achieved fame as a scientist. He was among the first persons in the world to experiment with electricity. In 1752, he conducted his well-known electrical experiment. He flew a homemade kite during a thunderstorm. A bolt of lightning struck the kite wire and traveled down to a key tied to the end. This caused a spark. This proved that lightning is electricity. (It should be noted that this is a very dangerous experiment: it should not be repeated.) Franklin then invented the lightning rod. The soundness of this invention was shown when lightning struck Franklin's home. The lightning rod saved the building from damage. Many authorities agree that Franklin was responsible for many electrical terms, such as armature, condenser, and battery.

Franklin's scientific interests were not concerned only with electricity. He became the first scientist to study the movement of the Gulf Stream in the Atlantic Ocean. He spent much time charting the Gulf's temperature, speed, and depth. Franklin showed naval officers and scientists that sailors could calm a rough sea by pouring oil on it.

Franklin invented several other devices besides the lightning rod. The Franklin stove proved very useful. By arranging the flues in his stove in a certain way, he made his sitting room twice as warm with one fourth as much fuel as he had been using. Franklin's invention of bifocal eyeglasses is used by people everywhere. This invention allowed both reading and distant lenses to be set in a single frame.

Franklin discovered that disease spreads rapidly in poorly ventilated rooms. He also showed that acid soil can be improved by using lime.

Benjamin Franklin refused to patent any of his inventions. He would not use them for profit. He preferred to have them used freely for the comfort and convenience of everyone.

Franklin's scientific work won him many honors. The Royal Society of London elected him to membership. This was a rare honor for a person living in the colonies.   J.J.A./D.G.F.

FREEZING AND FREEZING POINT A substance is freezing (frē′ zing) as it solidifies when heat is taken away from it. All substances but one freeze when they are cooled to low enough temperatures. Most gases, when cooled, become liquids at first. At an even lower temperature, the liquid becomes a solid. A few gases, such as carbon dioxide and iodine vapor, go straight to the solid stage. They skip the liquid stage. There is one substance that does not solidify, no matter how low the temperature. This is helium. It can only be solidified by being cooled under pressure. Without pressure, helium remains a liquid even at a fraction of a degree from absolute zero. The temperature at which a substance turns into a solid is called its freezing point. This is not always the temperature at which the solid melts. Supercooling may occur. This means that the liquid remains a liquid, even below its melting point.

If a substance is dissolved in a liquid, then the liquid freezes at a lower temperature. The greater the amount of substance dissolved, the lower the freezing point of the liquid. This effect is used to melt ice. When salt is scattered on the ice, the ice slowly dissolves. The salt solution has a lower freezing point than pure water. Therefore, if the temperature is not too low, the salt melts the ice. M.E./A.D.

Freezing points of some liquids and liquefied gases

	°C	°F		°C	°F
acetic acid	17	62	methyl alcohol	−94	−144
water	0	32	chlorine	−101	−150
seawater	−2	28	ethyl alcohol	−117	−179
bromine	−7	19	argon	−189	−308
ethylene glycol	−17	1	nitrogen	−210	−346
(antifreeze)			oxygen	−219	−362
ammonia	−78	−108	air	−223	−369
carbon dioxide	−78	−109	hydrogen	−259	−434
(gas to solid)			helium	−273	−459

FREEZING MIXTURE (frē′ zing miks′ chər) A freezing mixture is a mixture of substances used to produce a lowering of temperature. For example, a mixture of common salt (sodium chloride) and crushed ice is often used as a freezing mixture to produce temperatures as low as −20°C [−4°F]. As the salt dissolves in the water present in the mixture,

it takes up heat from the surroundings. The melting point of ice is lowered by the presence of the salt solution. The ice melts. As it does so, it absorbs heat from the surroundings. The surroundings are therefore cooled.

In the laboratory, a substance to be cooled is sometimes placed in a test tube and surrounded by a freezing mixture. *See also* LATENT HEAT. J.J.A./A.D.

FREON (frē′ än′) Freon is an artificial fluorocarbon compound, in the form of a gas or a liquid, that contains fluorine, carbon, and chlorine. Freons are used as propellants in aerosol products, and as refrigerants in air conditioners and refrigerators. Two of the most commonly used Freons are chlorofluoromethane ($CFCl_3$), also called F-11, and dichlorodifluoromethane (CF_2Cl_2), or F-12. Both are poisonous and nonflammable under normal conditions. Both are easily converted from gas to liquid, and from liquid to gas.

Scientific studies in the 1970s showed that F-11 and F-12 harm the environment. The chemicals in the two Freons escape to the upper atmosphere after being used primarily in aerosol products on earth. Ultraviolet rays cause the chemicals to break up in the upper atmosphere. Chlorine atoms are released and they attack and destroy ozone molecules. Ozone is a form of oxygen in the upper atmosphere that protects people and animals on earth by screening out the ultraviolet rays of the sun.

In 1977, the United States government banned the use of aerosol spray products using Freon propellants. W.R.P./J.M.

FREQUENCY (frē′ kwən sē) The frequency of an event is how often that event occurs. For example, the number of times that you go to school in a week is a frequency. The frequency may be five times per week. Scientists use the word ''frequency'' in connection with vibrations. If you pluck a guitar string, it vibrates. The number of times it vibrates in a second is its frequency. The frequency determines the pitch of the sound. A tightly-stretched string vibrates quickly. It produces a high note. A complete vibration is called a cycle. Sound waves that can be heard by humans vary from about 20 to 20,000 cycles per second. One cycle per second is equal to one hertz. (*See* HERTZ.)

There are many different kinds of electromagnetic radiation, such as X rays, visible light, and radio waves. These radiations are different because they have different frequencies. Radio waves have frequencies up to about a million million hertz. The frequencies of visible light are much greater than those of radio waves. They are about a million billion hertz. The frequencies of X rays are higher still. They are about a billion billion hertz. (*See* ELECTROMAGNETIC RADIATION.)

The distance between the start of one wave and the start of the next is called the wavelength. For example, the wavelength of waves on the sea is the distance between the top of one wave and the next. The speed of the wave can be found by multiplying the frequency by the wavelength. For any electromagnetic radiation, such as X rays, same for all frequencies. In a vacuum, it is 299,000 km per second [186,000 mi per second]. Visible light has a greater frequency

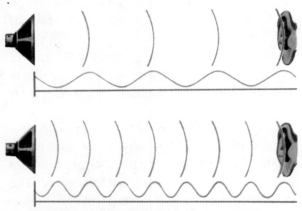

Top, a low note of 33 cycles/second is being produced. Bottom, the ear is receiving a note of higher frequency, 66 cycles/second.

than radio waves. But they both travel at the same speed. Therefore the wavelength of light is less than that of radio waves. The wavelength of radio waves is about 0.3 mm [about 0.012 in]. The speed of sound in air is around 330 m per second [1,100 ft per second]. This speed is the same for all frequencies. The frequencies of audible sound waves vary from about 20 to 20,000 hertz. Therefore, the wavelengths vary from about 15 m [50 ft] down to about 15 mm [0.6 in].

M.E./L.L.R.

Sigmund Freud

FREUD, SIGMUND (1856–1939) Sigmund Freud (fròid) was an Austrian doctor. His studies of the hidden workings of the human mind greatly advanced the treatment of mental illness. He began by using hypnosis to treat a mental condition called hysteria. He believed that mental illness was caused by fears and unpleasant thoughts that people have forgotten. The people do not want to think about these things, but they stay in their minds and can change their behavior. Freud treated mentally sick people by letting them relax and talk of anything they were thinking about. He believed that this helped them to get the hidden fears and thoughts out of their minds. This was the beginning of the science of psychoanalysis. Freud also believed that he could help people by getting them to remember dreams. He analyzed the dreams to understand what was worrying his patients. Freud later began to think that sexual problems were very important in causing mental illness. Some other psychiatrists, like Alfred Adler, did not agree with him about this.

Nowadays Freud's methods are still used for some diseases like neurosis. Doctors are careful to choose the right treatment for different mental illnesses. *See also* CONSCIOUSNESS; MENTAL HEALTH.   C.M./D.G.F.

FRICTION (frik′ shən) Friction is the force that resists the movement of one object over another. Friction is a very common effect in our lives. Without friction, automobiles would not be able to move. Their wheels would turn round on the same spot since they would not be able to grip the road. We would not be able to walk without friction. We can see this by comparing walking on a normal surface with walking on ice. There is much less friction between our feet and the ice. This lack of friction makes it very difficult to walk.

If you try to push a book along a table, the book does not move at first. You need to apply a force to overcome the friction between the book and the table. (*See* FORCE.) The book only moves after the force overcomes the friction. Without friction, the smallest force can cause the book to move. Once the book is moving, it slows down if the force is removed. The book is slowed down by friction. Without friction, the book would move even if the force were removed.

Most surfaces are not completely smooth. They are covered with tiny bumps. When two surfaces touch, these bumps tend to interlock. Before one of the surfaces can move, the interlocking has to be overcome. This is the cause of friction. Suppose that one of the materials is very hard and the other is very soft. When they touch, the bumps on the hard material push into the soft material and form "valleys" in it. At the same time, the soft

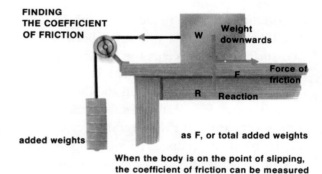

FINDING THE COEFFICIENT OF FRICTION

When the body is on the point of slipping, the coefficient of friction can be measured

These objects resist movement because of friction with the table surface. The force required to drag any one of them along is the same, because they all have the same weight and are made of the same material. Their shape does not affect their frictional reisistance as they move.

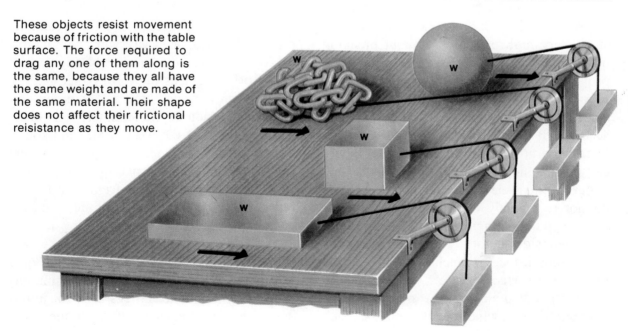

material is forced into the valleys of the hard material. This makes the shapes of their surfaces match up. The force needed to overcome this friction can be extremely large. Friction may also be caused by chemical bonds that are formed between the surfaces. Such bonds are responsible for the friction between liquids and solids or gases and solids, for example. These bonds have to be broken before the friction is overcome. (*See* BOND, CHEMICAL.)

The frictional force between two objects does not depend on the amount of surface in contact. For example, suppose a book on its side is pushed along a table. There is a frictional force between the two. The book is then placed on its end and pushed along. The force of friction between the book and the table remains the same.

Friction can be reduced by lubrication. The lubricant forms a thin layer between the two surfaces. It prevents the bumps and valleys from interlocking. There is still some friction between the lubricant and the surface, but it is much less. Lubricants can be solids, liquids, or gases. In a Hovercraft, a cushion of air is used to reduce friction. (*See* AIR-CUSHION VEHICLE.) In some heavy machinery, graphite is used as a lubricant. Graphite is a form of carbon. It is a solid and can withstand very high pressures without breaking down chemically. This is a very important property for any lubricant. The most common lubricant is oil. Oil is an excellent lubricant since it greatly reduces the friction between surfaces. It is widely used in engineering. If there were no lubricant used, friction would cause machine parts to become hotter and hotter and to wear away quickly. Engineers do not rely solely on lubricants to reduce friction. Ball bearings are used if one part has to rotate inside another. The friction between two rolling surfaces is much less than between two sliding surfaces.

Friction also plays a part in the weather. Without friction, wind speeds would be much greater. The molecules in the air are slowed down by friction with the earth's surface. Friction affects the wind speed at heights up to 500 meters [549 yd]. Above this height, wind speeds can be twice what they are on the ground.   M.E./J.T.

The frigate bird has a seven-foot wingspan and is a very acrobatic flyer.

FRIGATE BIRD (frig′ ət bərd) Frigate birds are dark-colored seabirds that belong to the family Fregatidae. They live by the ocean, nesting in large colonies on islands. Frigate birds are strong fliers and are able to soar long distances without moving their wings. They never land on the water, however, because they cannot take off from water. Because of this, frigate birds scoop up fish, their food, from the water's surface while they are still flying. Often, a frigate bird will not catch its own fish but steal one away from another bird.

There is only one species of frigate bird found off the coasts of North America. The magnificent frigate bird is common off southern Florida in the summer. It is occasionally seen off the west, Gulf, and southeastern coasts. It reaches lengths of 87 cm [35 in] and has a wingspan up to 2.25 m [7 ft]. The male magnificent frigate bird has a red throat pouch which is inflated during courtship.   S.R.G./M.L.

FROG (frȯg) The popular description of a frog is that it is an amphibian with smooth, slippery skin and strong legs used for jumping. (*See* AMPHIBIAN.) Although there are

Above, this tree frog is found on the east coast of Africa. It measures about 3.75 cm [1.5 in] long.

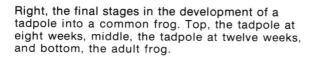

Right, the final stages in the development of a tadpole into a common frog. Top, the tadpole at eight weeks, middle, the tadpole at twelve weeks, and bottom, the adult frog.

many families of frogs throughout the world, the true frogs of North America belong to the family Ranidae. Frogs are able to crawl out of water. They must, however, keep their skin wet so they usually do not travel far from water. Usually, they sit in shallow water or in the wet grass near the pond's edge, waiting for an insect to fly by. Frogs catch insects by shooting out their long tongues. Small fish, snakes, and other frogs are also eaten. Frogs lay many eggs in water. The eggs hatch into tadpoles, which swim like fish until they change into adult frogs. Frogs that live in colder climates hibernate during winter. (*See* HIBERNATION.) The bullfrog, the largest frog in North America, is often raised for food. Many fine restaurants serve frogs' legs. *See also* BULLFROG; TOAD.   S.R.G./R.L.L.

FRONT (frənt) A front is the boundary between two different air masses. The air masses differ in such variables as temperature or dew point.

In the northern hemisphere, warm air from the south is separated from the colder arctic air by the polar front. Here, the heavy cold air is constantly pushing underneath the lighter warm air. The mixing of the warm and cold air produces clouds and precipitation (rain or snow) along the polar front. If the jet stream conditions are right, a depression may develop. (*See* DEPRESSION.)

The leading edge of the warm air is called a warm front. It is usually preceded by a period of continuous rain or snow. At the warm front, fog often occurs. The advancing edge of the cold air is called a cold front. Just ahead of a cold front is an area of thunderstorms and possibly tornadoes, called a squall line. The bad weather associated with a cold front is usually brief. After the cold front passes, the weather turns colder, and strong winds blow from the northwest in the northern hemisphere.

Sometimes, the air at a front does not mix, and the front stalls. This is called a stationary front. When a cold front catches up to a warm front, it pushes all the warm air above the cold air. This is called an occluded front. *See also* CYCLONE; METEOROLOGY.   J.M.C./C.R.

FROST (fròst) Frost is made of ice crystals that coat objects on the earth's surface. Frost forms in a way similar to dew. On a clear, still night, when the dew point drops below 0°C [32°F], water vapor in the air changes directly to the solid state by a process called sublimation. This results in the deposit of ice crystals on available surfaces. The deposit is called frost, or hoarfrost.

Each year, frost injures fruit grown in the southern United States and California. Some fruit growers use heaters that raise the temperature of the air around the plants, thus preventing frost damage. *See also* METEOROLOGY. J.M.C./C.R.

FRUIT

All flowering plants produce fruits (früts). A fruit is a mature ovary with its enclosed seeds. It is produced by the flower. As a result of pollination, a pollen nucleus fertilizes an egg in the ovary of the pistil. (*See* FERTILIZATION.) This fertilized egg develops into a seed. At the same time, other changes are taking place in the flower. The anther and the stigma begin to waste away. The petals and the sepals usually drop off. Most importantly, though, the ovary begins to get larger as it develops into the fruit.

There are many types of fruits, but they all have the same functions. They protect the developing seeds, and help disperse these seeds. (*See* DISPERSION OF PLANTS.)

Types of fruits Fruits are either dry or fleshy, depending on the wall surrounding the seeds. This fruit wall is called the pericarp. Dry fruits have a dry, usually woody, pericarp. The seeds of dry fruits are used for food. Fleshy fruits have a juicy, edible pericarp that is used for food. The seeds of fleshy fruits are usually inedible.

Dry fruits are either dehiscent or indehis-cent. (*See* DEHISCENCE.) Dehiscent fruits open when the seeds reach maturity. This releases the seeds for dispersion by the wind or other agents. Dehiscent fruits may be capsules which split along three seams, legumes which split along two seams, or follicles which split along one seam. Indehiscent fruits remain closed and do not release the mature seeds. Nuts and grains are the most familiar of the indehiscent fruits.

Fleshy fruits may develop from one or more ovaries from one or more flowers. Fleshy fruits may be berries, drupes, or pomes. Berries develop from one or more pistils. They have a fleshy pericarp and small seeds. Citrus fruits, grapes, and tomatoes are all berries. Multiple berries are formed from the pistils of many flowers joined together. Pineapples are an example of a multiple berry. Drupes are formed from one pistil. The pericarp is fleshy, but its inner part is a hard, woody pit or stone. Apricots, cherries, peaches, and plums are drupes. Blackberries and raspberries are actually collections of tiny drupes which develop from several pistils of one flower. A pome or accessory fruit develops from structures other than just the pistil. For example, apples and pears are pomes. The juicy, edible pericarp comes from the receptacle of the flower. The pistils form the tough core which contains the seeds. The strawberry is another type of accessory fruit because the fleshy pericarp comes mostly from the upper part of the stem. Since pomes or accessory fruits develop from structures other than just the pistil, they are sometimes called false fruits.

Importance of fruits Fruits form an important part of a balanced diet. They provide carbohydrates, vitamins, and minerals. Fleshy fruits are a good source of water and contain large amounts of cellulose. Cellulose is not digested by the human body, and provides part of the roughage needed in the diet. Most fruits are tasty and, except for the cellulose, are easily digested.

The United States produces and uses more fruit than any other country in the world. Until fairly recently, people were able to buy only those fruits which were native to their area, and only during certain times of the year. As food preservation methods became more sophisticated, however, consumers have been offered a wide variety of fruits year round.

Selective breeding is used to develop new varieties of fruits and to improve the quality of current varieties. (*See* GENETICS; HEREDITY.) Many of the most popular fruits are actually hybrids produced after years of experimentation. Seedless fruits are popular with consum-ers, but must be reproduced by special methods. (*See* VEGETATIVE PROPAGATION.)

Fruit or vegetable? Although botanists have a definite way of defining "fruit," the word is commonly misused to indicate just fleshy fruits. Beans and tomatoes are usually considered vegetables even though they contain seeds and are, by definition, fruits. A fruit is any seed-containing structure produced by the ovary of a flowering plant. In some cases, a fruit may be seedless, but it always comes from the pistil of a flower. A vegetable is any other edible part of a plant, such as the leaves, roots, or stem.   A.J.C./M.H.S.

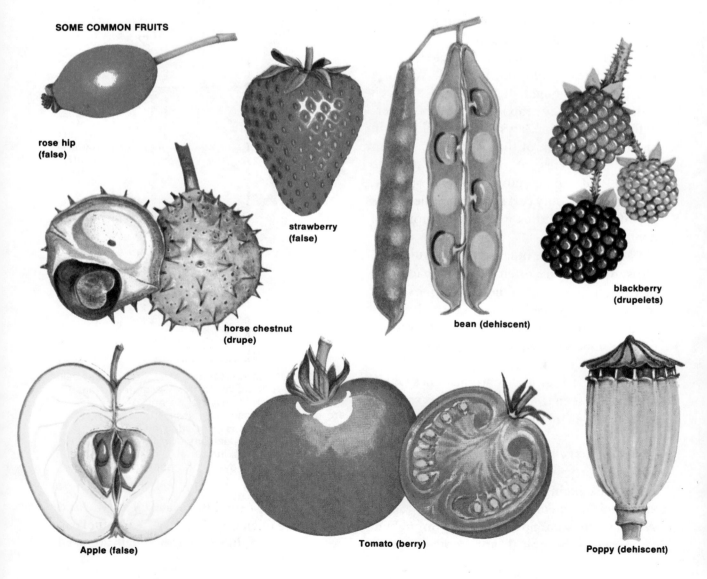

SOME COMMON FRUITS

rose hip
(false)

strawberry
(false)

horse chestnut
(drupe)

bean (dehiscent)

blackberry
(drupelets)

Apple (false)

Tomato (berry)

Poppy (dehiscent)

FRUIT FLY (früt flī) Fruit fly is the name given to two separate families of small flies, Tephritidae and Drosophilidae, that cause extensive damage to fruit. (*See* FLY.) The larvae of some members of the family Tephritidae feed on orchard fruits. The most important of these flies is the Mediterranean fruit fly (*Ceratitis capitata*). It lives in warm areas throughout the world. It has a large head with large, green, compound eyes. The head is attached to the dark, bristly body by a tiny neck. The female lays about 500 eggs at a time in various fruits, especially citrus fruits. Within days, the eggs hatch into maggots which destroy the fruit. (*See* LARVAE.) When the fruit falls to the ground, the insect lives as a pupa in the soil, finally becoming an adult. The cycle then begins again.

These pests were first detected in the United States in Florida, in 1929. Within a year, it was thought that they had all been killed. When they reappeared in 1956, international quarantine laws were established in an attempt to control their spread.

Other species of Tephritidae damage cherry and apple crops. Some species, though, attack only certain weeds. These flies are often imported as a means of biological control.

Members of the other family of fruit flies, Drosophilidae, are often called pomace flies or vinegar flies because they sometimes breed in fermenting juices such as crushed grapes used for making wine. They reproduce quickly. One species, *Drosophila melanogaster,* is used extensively in genetic research because it has four large chromosomes which are easily seen in cells from the salivary glands. *See also* HEREDITY.   A.J.C./J.E.R.

FUCHSIA (fyü′ shə) Fuchsia is a genus of about 100 species of flowering shrubs belonging to the evening primrose family. Native to sub-tropical areas of North and South America, they are now cultivated throughout temperate, sub-tropical, and tropical regions of the world. Some species grow as tall as 12 m [40 ft]. Most have opposite or whorled leaves measuring about 5 cm [2 in] long. The drooping flowers grow from the axils. They have a long, colored calyx tube and a corolla of four petals, usually of a different color. The blossoms are about 5 cm [2 in] long, and in wild varieties, are red or purple. Cultivated fuchsias may be any of several colors. Some species of fuchsia are called lady's-eardrops. They are often grown as houseplants.
A.J.C./M.H.S.

This diagram shows the simplest kind of fuel cell containing a liquid electrolyte—a material that conducts electricity. Hydrogen and oxygen gases are fed into the cell. On passing the catalyst, the hydrogen dissociates into hydrogen ions, H^+, and electrons, e^-. The electrons flow through an external circuit, making an electric current. The hydrogen atoms move to the opposite electrode.

FUEL (fyül) A fuel is a material that is used as a source of energy. The energy in a fuel can be put to many different uses. Fuels are used to drive engines in automobiles, airplanes, trains, and ships. In these engines, the fuel is usually mixed with air and burned. When a fuel burns, it gives off a large amount of heat. This heat is used to drive the engine. It can also be used for warmth or to drive other kinds of machines. For example, the heat can be used to turn water into steam. The steam may then be used to drive a turbine. The turbine, in turn, can drive a generator to produce electricity. In this way, the energy of a fuel can be converted into electrical energy. There are many different kinds of fuels. They can be divided into solid fuels, liquid fuels, and gaseous fuels.

Solid fuels   Solid fuels include wood, coal, coke, and peat. Wood has been used as a fuel for thousands of years. It was the first fuel to be used by people. Few countries rely on it as a fuel now. Coal is a much more important fuel. It, too, has been used for many years. It was used for smelting metals in 400 B.C. Coke is made by heating coal without any air being present. Peat is a soft substance with fibers. It occurs in peat bogs in several parts of the world. It is used as a fuel only in a few countries, such as Ireland. Paraffin and tallow are two other kinds of solid fuel. They are used mainly for candles.

Heat value is the name given to the amount of heat energy a certain quantity of fuel can produce. In the graph below, heat values for different kinds of fuels are shown. The heat value of a solid or liquid fuel depends on its chemical makeup and on the amount of water and ash it contains. Peat has more water than coal, so it has a lower heat value than coal.

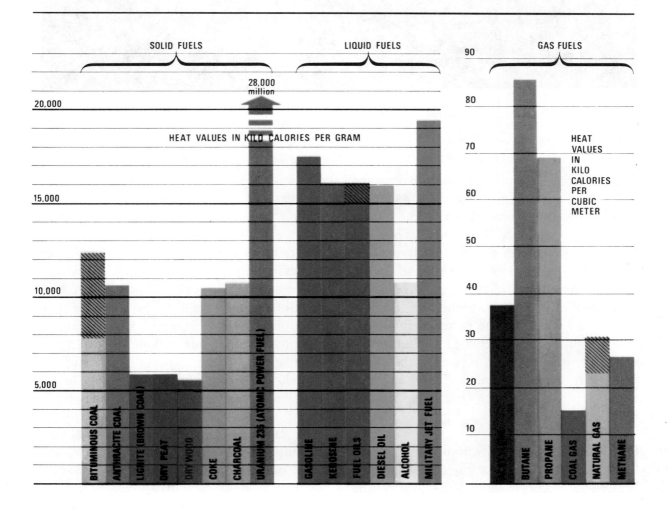

Coal mines usually consist of underground tunnels, such as the one shown here. The coal is moved from the pit to the surface in trucks.

Liquid fuels Most liquid fuels are obtained from petroleum. An example is gasoline, which is used in automobiles. Liquid fuels can also be obtained from coal. They are given off when coal is converted into coke. Benzene is one such fuel. It is used in certain internal combustion engines. In some countries, alcohol is used as a liquid fuel. Usually it is mixed with gasoline before being used. Oils obtained from vegetables and animal fat were once used for fuel. However, they burn with a very smoky flame. They are also rather expensive and are no longer used for fuel now.

Gaseous fuels The most important gaseous fuels are natural gas, coal gas, and water gas. Natural gas occurs in large deposits under the ground. It is a very convenient source of fuel and is widely used. Coal gas is a mixture of gases that are given off when coal is converted into coke. For a time, natural gas replaced coal gas as a fuel for homes and factories. As natural gas supplies continue to decrease, however, coal gas will again be used, more and more. Water gas is a mixture of hydrogen and carbon monoxide. It is made by passing steam over red-hot coke. It is used in industry. Butane gas is a convenient source of fuel. It is obtained from natural gas. Butane is compressed into containers and used as a portable source of fuel, especially by campers. Gaseous fuels are very clean. They do not produce much smoke or ash when they burn.

New fuels Industrial countries are now burning enormous amounts of coal, gas, and oil. The earth's supply of these fuels may soon be used up. Scientists are now looking for other sources of fuel. The metal uranium is a new fuel and is now being used on a large scale. Uranium is radioactive and its radioactivity can be converted into other forms of energy. Other radioactive fuels are also being used. Radioactive fuels contain large amounts of energy.

The energy in fuels such as coal, gas, and oil is chemical energy. Chemical energy comes from the bonds which hold the atoms together. Radioactive fuels contain nuclear energy. This energy comes from the force that holds the nucleus together. (*See* NUCLEAR POWER.) The bonds that hold the nucleus together are stronger than the bonds that hold atoms together. Therefore, radioactive materials contain much more energy than substances such as coal. However, even our uranium supplies will not last forever. Scientists are now trying to control thermonuclear energy. This is the energy that makes the sun and other stars shine. Thermonuclear energy could be obtained from hydrogen. Water is a compound of hydrogen and oxygen and there are huge amounts of water on the earth. Hydrogen could be extracted from this water and this would give us a virtually unlimited supply of energy. But there are many difficult technical problems to be solved first. Another possibility is not to use a fuel for energy at all. The sun gives off large amounts of energy as heat and light. This energy is called solar energy. It is possible to convert solar energy into electrical energy. So far, this has only been done on a very small scale. Geothermal energy flows from the hot interior of the earth to the surface. In a few places, pipes buried at great depths bring superheated steam to the surface to drive turbines to generate electricity. Near Reykjavik, Iceland, hot water from geothermal wells is used to heat buildings. Tidal power is another possibility. But again, there are many difficulties to be overcome first. M.E./J.M.

FUEL CELL (fyül' sel) Fuel cells are devices used to generate electricity. They do this by converting the energy given off in a chemical reaction into electrical energy. Automobile storage batteries and dry cells also obtain electricity from chemical reactions. (*See* BATTERY.) But storage batteries and dry cells run down after a while and have to be replaced or recharged. Fuel cells do not run down so long as they are supplied with fuel.

The first fuel cell was built in 1839. It used hydrogen and oxygen as fuels. However, the invention was neglected for more than a century. Hydrogen and oxygen combine to form water. When they combine, they give off energy. The fuel cell converts this energy into electricity. It works on the opposite principle to electrolysis. In electrolysis, an electric current is passed through a liquid. If the liquid is water, the current causes the water to break down into hydrogen and oxygen.

Modern fuel cells use liquid hydrogen and liquid oxygen. They can be stored in a much smaller space than gaseous hydrogen and oxygen. Another advantage is that the liquids can be made much purer than the gases. Scientists are experimenting with different sorts of fuel cells.

Fuel cells have been used for several years as a souce of power in manned spacecraft. They were used in the Apollo missions. The crew used the water produced by the fuel cell for drinking. Fuel cells are also used to power lamps in remote buoys at sea. Electric cars have been designed so that they can be powered by fuel cells. Fuel cells do not produce air-polluting smoke and so would be ideal for an automobile. M.E./A.D.

FULLER'S EARTH (fül' ərz ərth) Fuller's earth is claylike matter consisting of 50 to 80% silica. Fuller's earth absorbs grease and oil and is used for the bleaching and purification of petroleum and household oils. Fuller's earth is so named because it was once used to remove grease from wool by a process called fulling. J.M.C./W.R.S.

FULMAR (ful' mər) The fulmar is a gull-like sea bird with thick feathers and a hooked, yellow bill. The bill has tubular nostrils and looks much like that of the albatross. The fulmar has webbed feet and a claw formed from the hind toe. Fulmars fly just above the surface of the ocean looking for living or dead animal matter. One of their favorite foods is whale blubber. For this reason, fulmars often follow whaling boats, eating the scraps and discarded wastes.

The northern fulmar (*Fulmar glacialis*) nests in rocky cliffs near the Arctic circle. It sometimes migrates as far south as Cape Cod in Massachusetts. The female lays one egg each year. She often protects her nest by spitting a bad-smelling oily liquid at potential enemies. For this reason, fulmars are sometimes called foul-gulls. A.J.C./M.L.

FULTON, ROBERT (1765–1815) Robert Fulton (ful' tən) was an American engineer. He was born in Little Britain, Pennsylvania. He began work as a portrait painter. In 1786 he went to London, England, to study with the American painter Benjamin West. While he was in England he became interested in canals. Because nobody in England was interested in his canal inventions, he went to France in 1797.

His next idea was for a torpedo, but this was not used by the French or English. The French Emperor Napoleon asked Fulton to design a submarine. This was built in 1800 and was named the *Nautilus*. While it was underwater, everything on the *Nautilus* was worked by hand. It was submerged by men letting water into tanks. The propeller which moved it underwater was driven by a man turning a wheel. To make it surface, men had to pump the water out of the tanks. It had sails for traveling on the surface. The *Nautilus* was very hard to work and was never used in battle.

Fulton is most famous for building steamships. He built his first steamship in Paris, France, in 1803. Then he went back to England for two years. Finally Fulton returned to America. His first successful steamship was called the *Clermont*. It was launched on the Hudson River in 1807 and made the 150-mile trip from New York to Albany in 32 hours. C.M./D.G.F.

FUNGICIDE (fən' jə sīd') A fungicide is a type of chemical pesticide used to kill harmful types of fungi. (*See* FUNGUS.) Fungi cause many diseases in plants, animals, and human beings. Large amounts of crops are destroyed each year by fungi such as blight, mildew, mold, and smut. Some seeds become infected with fungi which prevent them from germinating. (*See* GERMINATION.) Two common and very contagious human diseases caused by parasitic fungi are ringworm and athlete's foot. The plant diseases are usually controlled by spraying the crops with fungicides. The human diseases can be treated with special fungicidal ointments and powders. Antibiotics are sometimes used to kill fungi. Unfortunately, antibiotics also kill the helpful bacteria which usually keep the fungi under control.

Fungicides are either inorganic or organic. Inorganic fungicides use compounds of metals such as copper and mercury to kill fungi. Organic fungicides, such as formaldehyde, are made of poisonous chemicals combined with carbon, hydrogen, and oxygen. Some natural substances are also used as fungicides. Creosote, an oily substance from the creosote bush, is often painted on wood that is exposed to water. This helps prevent dry rot, a fungus-caused disease of the wood.

It is important that fungicides kill fungi but do not harm plants or animals. Since many fungicides are poisonous, they are often used in controlled, limited areas. Most foods that have been sprayed with fungicides must be washed carefully before being eaten. *See also* HERBICIDE; INSECTICIDE; PESTICIDE; POISON. A.J.C./F.W.S.

FUNGUS

A fungus (fəng′ gəs) is a simple, non-green plant that has no roots, stems, leaves, or flowers. The fungi are a large group of different kinds of organisms that have some of the characteristics of primitive plants, such as algae, and of animallike organisms, such as protozoans. They are not, however, closely related to either of these two groups. Traditionally, fungi were classified in a sub-kingdom of the plant kingdom. Now, modern classification places them in a kingdom of their own, Fungi. (*See* CLASSIFICATION OF LIVING ORGANISMS.) More than 100,000 species of fungi are known.

Fungi are extremely versatile organisms.

They live throughout the world in every imaginable climate and environment. Some familiar fungi are blight, mushrooms, molds, yeasts, mildews, rusts, and smuts. Slime molds are often considered fungi, though this classification is the source of some disagreement.

Structure of the fungus Some of the primitive, one-celled fungi are actually spore cases which are anchored by means of tiny filaments called rhizoids. Some of these fungi, such as yeast, do not even form rhizoids. Most fungi, however, have a body called a thallus. The thallus is made up of thousands of tiny, hairlike cells called hyphae. These hyphae are usually white and contain no chlorophyll. The hyphae are bunched together to form a mycelium. The mycelium usually lodges inside a source of nutrition

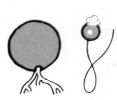

A small, primitive water fungus *Rhizophidium*. The adult fungus (left) is a cyst, or bag, anchored by tubes called rhizoids. The mature cyst releases zoospores (right), which either develop into a cyst or pair together to form a zygote.

A simple land fungus, *Sporodinia*. It differs from Rhizophidium in that it has a network of tubes called a mycelium. The adult form can reproduce in either a sexual (forming gametes) or an asexual (forming spores) manner. The adult fungus (top) releases asexual spores that develop into the mycelium. The adult form may put out branches of different "sexes" (bottom) that come together to form zygospores, as shown.

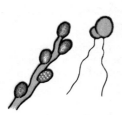

The primitive water fungus, *Allomyces*. The adult fungus (left) has sporangia, tiny bags that release zoospores. These spores develop into another life-stage which, in turn, releases male and female cells, called gametes.

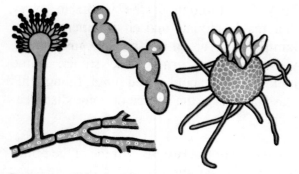

Three kinds of ascomycetes, fungi that sometimes reproduce sexually by means of an ascus, or spore sac. Left: *Aspergillus*, a common blue mold that usually reproduces asexually by conidiospores, which are arranged in chains on a conidiophore, or hypha branch. Middle: yeast cells reproducing asexually by budding. Right: an ascomycete with a sexual structure called cleistothecium (orange part), which releases several asci (blue part).

such as a plant, an animal, or the soil. Often, a large fruiting body grows from the mycelium. The fruiting body contains many spores which, when released, will grow into new fungi. In the mushroom, the mycelium is underground where it receives nutrition from the soil. The fruiting body is the umbrella-shaped structure that grows above the ground. It is this fruiting body that is often considered the ''mushroom.'' Fungi range in size from a microscopic yeast cell at 0.0001 mm [0.000004 in] to a giant species of mushroom measuring more than 95 cm [38 in] across.

Life of the fungus   Since fungi contain no chlorophyll, they cannot produce their own food. (*See* PHOTOSYNTHESIS.) They must, therefore, get food from some other source. In order for a fungus to ''eat,'' it secretes enzymes into its food. These enzymes start the digestion of complex foods into simple compounds. The fungus then absorbs these digested foods into its hyphae.

Different species of fungi get their food from different sources and in different ways. Parasitic fungi feed on living plants and animals. (*See* PARASITE.) Parasitic fungi cause many diseases in their hosts, and usually have

to be controlled with fungicides. Saprophytic fungi feed on dead and decaying plant and animal matter. (*See* SAPROPHYTE.) They are vital parts of the food chain. Symbiotic fungi share a mutually helpful relationship with some other organism. (*See* SYMBIOSIS.) Lichens are symbiotic algae and fungi. Mycorrhiza is a fungus living symbiotically in the roots of many forest plants. The roots give the fungus shelter, food, and water. The fungus, on the other hand, supplies nitrogen, zinc, phosphorous, and other minerals to the plant.

Most fungi reproduce asexually by producing spores that grow into new fungi. Some fungi, such as yeast, reproduce asexually by budding. Others split by fission. (*See* ASEXUAL REPRODUCTION.) Some fungi produce spores which act like gametes. They combine to form a zygote which develops into an adult. A few species of fungi have a sexually reproductive stage which alternates with an asexual stage. (*See* ALTERNATION OF GENERATIONS.)

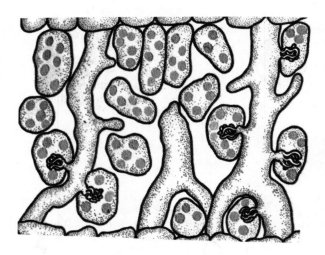

Many fungi are plant parasites. This diagram of a green leaf shows how the mycelium of a fungus invades a leaf and puts out rootlike haustoria that penetrate the leaf cells to obtain food.

Importance of fungi   Fungi can be harmful or helpful to human beings and other organisms. Parasitic fungi cause many harmful

This parasitic fungus, called *Tremella,* grows on the bark of trees. It has a lobed sporophore, or fruit-body, which can be orange, brown, or whitish in color. It is jellylike in texture. Many fungi are brightly colored.

plant diseases such as blight, mildew, mold, rust, and smut. Blight destroyed the potato crop in Ireland in the 1840s. This caused a famine in which about 750,000 people starved to death. Mold ruins millions of dollars worth of food, both processed and unprocessed, every year. (*See* FOOD PRESERVATION.) In addition to the damage it causes to plants, mildew can destroy clothing and books stored in damp places.

One type of plant fungus, ergot, grows on rye and other grains. It can be processed to produce several powerful drugs, including LSD. LSD, lysergic acid diethylamide, is a dangerous hallucinogen that has many side effects. (*See* HALLUCINATION.) Ergotism, or St. Anthony's fire, is a disease that affects people and animals that eat grains infected with ergot fungus. This disease is incurable and causes convulsions and death. Some diseases, such as ringworm and athlete's foot, are caused by a fungus which is easily passed from one person to another. Many varieties of mushrooms are poisonous and can cause sickness or death if eaten. (*See* POISON.)

There are many helpful types of fungi, however. Saprophytic fungi (along with bacteria) are an important part of the food chain. In the process of getting food for themselves, they help decompose dead plant and animal matter. (*See* DECOMPOSITION.) They break down food into simple molecules, releasing many minerals and other chemicals needed at this stage of the food chain.

Some fungi are, themselves, used as foods. Mushrooms are a popular food in most parts of the world. They grow rapidly and are easily cultivated. Certain molds are added to cheeses such as camembert and roquefort to provide a sharp flavor and to help ripen the cheese. Yeasts are eaten as a source of protein and B vitamins. As food research continues, yeast may someday be a major nutrient source. (*See* DIET.) Yeasts are also used in fermentation of certain grains to produce alcoholic beverages. (*See* ALCOHOL.) In fermentation, yeast changes sugar into carbon dioxide gas and alcohol. The carbon dioxide provides the carbonation (bubbling) in many beverages. Yeast is also used in bread products, releasing carbon dioxide, and causing the dough to rise.

Some molds are used to produce antibiotics and other drugs. The most famous of these, penicillin, was processed from a mold in 1929.   A.J.C./M.H.S.

FURNACE (fər′ nəs) A furnace is any enclosed structure in which fuel is burned to produce heat. A furnace is usually made of metal or brick, or a combination of these or other fireproof substances. Furnaces are de-

signed to produce the greatest amount of heat from the fuel used. They are also designed to direct the heat where it is most needed. Furnaces are used to produce heat for comfort. They are also used to boil water to make steam, or to heat various substances.

There are two main groups of furnaces. The first group consists of furnaces used for heating homes. Warm air furnaces may burn several fuels, such as coal, coke, gas, or oil. These fuels heat air. The air then rises through large tubes called ducts to openings, or registers, in the various rooms. When cool, the air returns through a cold-air register to the furnace. A forced-air furnace has a blower. The blower directs and increases the flow of warm air. Another type of furnace is connected to a steam boiler. This type heats water until steam forms. The steam passes through pipes

This high temperature furnace is used for melting metals. It was designed to heat several tons of metal at one time.

The interior of an electric arc furnace. The glare in the center is the arc produced between two electrodes. Molten metal is underneath.

to various rooms. Other furnaces, connected to hot-water boilers, do not heat water to the boiling point. They aid in circulating hot water through pipes and radiators. A forced hot-water system uses a pump. The pump works to force the water through the pipes. This gives a faster circulation.

Home furnaces must be cared for regularly. Cleaning furnaces maintains their efficiency. It also helps to prevent fires. All furnaces, chimneys, and air ducts should be serviced once every year. The sealing of furnace joints should be periodically checked.

The second group of furnaces, which are those used in industry, are used mainly to heat metals and make steam. They are also used in making cement, glass, bricks, steel, and many other materials. Industrial furnaces produce extremely high temperatures. Many of them use coal or coke for fuel. Others use gas, oil, or electricity. One industrial furnace, the blast furnace, is a cone-shaped structure of brick, concrete, and steel. The blast furnace is used to fuse, or melt, iron ore with coke to make pig iron. It is also used to make iron from iron ore. Fans blow air under pressure into the furnace. This makes the fire extremely hot.

Electric furnaces are widely used. Metalworkers often need temperatures ranging from 1,830°C to 2,800°C [3,500°F to 5,000°F]. Electric furnaces can produce these temperatures. There are three main types of electric furnaces. In arc furnaces, heat comes from an electric arc formed between carbon electrodes. A resistance furnace works like a bread toaster. A resistance furnace produces heat by passing an electric current through a substance. The substance, in resisting the electric current, becomes very hot. An induction furnace sends an alternating current through a conductor. (*See* INDUCTION.) The conductor is wrapped around an insulated container. The container holds the material that is to be heated, usually melted. The alternating current produces a changing magnetic field. (*See* ELECTROMAGNETISM.) This changing magnetic field causes a current to flow in the material. The induced current heats the material. If a material, such as glass, does not allow induced currents to be set up with it, the container is usually made of carbon. In these cases, the induction furnace produces heat within the container. In turn, the container melts the material.

Atomic furnaces or nuclear reactors are designed to produce power by nuclear fission. Their fuel is usually uranium or plutonium.

Solar furnaces produce temperatures of 4,400°C [8,000°F] or higher. In a solar furnace, a certain group of mirrors focuses the sun's rays to a specific spot in an oven. (*See* SOLAR ENERGY.) *See also* CENTRAL HEATING; KILN.

J.J.A./R.W.L.

FUSE, ELECTRIC An electric fuse (fyüz) is a device that breaks an electric circuit when the current becomes too strong because of a short, or an overload. A short occurs when two wires supplying electricity in a house accidentally touch one another. A large surge

of current flows through the wires. This can cause the wires to heat up and start a fire. (*See* RESISTANCE, ELECTRICAL.) An overload occurs when too many appliances are plugged into a single circuit. Again, the wires of the circuit are carrying more current than they can safely handle. The fuse prevents these occurrences from happening.

The fuse usually consists of a thin, metal strip or wire that is attached to two terminals inside a cylindrical housing. The housing either screws or plugs into an electric circuit between the main power line and the house wiring. Electric current flows into the house circuit only when the fuse is in place and is in working order. When a surge of current flows through the metal strip in the fuse, it quickly melts. The strip is a special alloy that melts at low temperature. A gap is created in the strip. This prevents an electric current from flowing into the house circuit where it could cause trouble. Thus, an electric fuse is a kind of circuit breaker.

There are two kinds of house fuses: plug fuses and cartridge fuses. Both types have small windows so that it is possible to see if the metal strip is still in one piece. Plug fuses screw into sockets and carry light electrical loads. They are used in circuits that supply current for lights and small appliances. Cartridge fuses are long, narrow cylinders that slide into spring-loaded brackets. They carry heavier electrical loads for items such as electric stoves and clothes washers. Fuses are found mainly in older houses. Most modern houses are required to have circuit breakers.

Fuses are rated for the maximum current they can carry. Most house fuses are rated between 15 and 25 amperes. If a low-rated fuse is placed in a higher-rated circuit, it burns out immediately. A high-rated fuse in a lower-rated circuit is dangerous. It allows too much current to flow into the circuit. The excess current can burn out small appliances and cause wires to overheat. Sometimes, people try to replace a burned out plug fuse with a copper penny. The penny closes the circuit and allows current to flow. However, the penny does nothing to prevent a short or overload. *See also* CIRCUIT, ELECTRIC.

W.R.P./J.T.

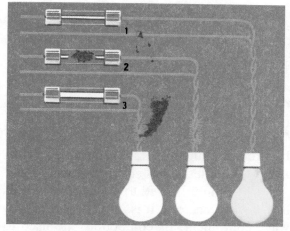

In a normal circuit (1), a small electric current flows through the fuse (left), the wire, and the bulb and back again. If a fault or short circuit occurs (2), a large current flows, and the fuse burns out. If the fuse is too thick, it remains intact, and the wire starts to burn (3).

FUSION (fyü′ zhən) Fusion means melting. It means the change that takes place when a solid turns into a liquid. The melting of ice is fusion. So is the melting of any metal when it is heated. Fusion is the opposite of freezing, or solidification.

Heat energy is required to produce fusion. The heat energy absorbed during fusion helps to separate the molecules of a substance. The molten substance has a greater energy content than it had when it was solid. A pound of water contains more energy than a pound of ice. The temperature of a substance does not change while it is actually melting. The heat that is supplied all goes to increasing the distance between the molecules, so that they move more freely. The amount of heat needed to change a unit mass of solid into liquid at the same temperature is called the specific latent heat of fusion. The latent heats of fusion of different substances have been measured.

They are important to chemists, physicists, and engineers.

Nuclear fusion   The term fusion is also used by nuclear physicists. When they use it, it means more than melting. It means melting together, or simply joining together. Nuclear fusion means the joining together of two or more atomic nuclei. (*See* NUCLEUS.) This is a kind of reaction in which nuclear energy is released. The other kind of atomic reaction is called nuclear fission. This means splitting a nucleus.

In nuclear fusion, the nuclei of atoms of low atomic weight are made to join together. The conditions must be just right. If they are, the nuclei form the nucleus of a new atom. The new atom is an atom of a different element. It has a higher atomic weight. When fusion takes place like this, a great amount of energy is released. The energy of the hydrogen bomb is produced by nuclear fusion.

The simplest kind of nuclear fusion uses the atomic nuclei of deuterium. Deuterium is ''heavy hydrogen.'' Each nucleus has a neutron as well as a proton (ordinary hydrogen has only a proton as its nucleus). If two deuterium nuclei can be made to join, they may form the nucleus of an isotope of the helium atom and a neutron. The nucleus of a helium atom contains only one neutron. So for every two nuclei that fuse, there is a neutron left over. All the energy that kept the neutron in place in its deuterium nucleus is suddenly released.

The amount of energy needed to keep a neutron inside a nucleus is very great. Unless the fusion reaction is properly under control, the energy could be very destructive. It could produce an explosion like a hydrogen bomb. If the energy can be controlled, however, it can be a tremendous advantage to us. It can help to solve the planet's energy problems.

We have no problem in obtaining deuterium. It is a fairly common isotope of hydrogen. We have all that we need in the water of the oceans. Our main problem is

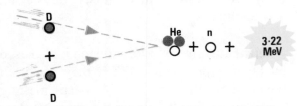

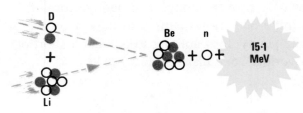

Nuclear fusion occurs when two light atomic nuclei join together to form a heavier nucleus, releasing energy in the process. Left, two deuterium nuclei, each with one proton and one neutron, collide to form a helium nucleus and a neutron, releasing much energy. Right, a deuterium nucleus collides with a lithium nucleus. The nuclei fuse to form a beryllium nucleus and a neutron, releasing even more energy.

getting the reaction to work, and keeping it under control.

In a fusion reaction, two nuclei have to be pushed together. This is difficult because the nuclei both have positive electrical charges. They repel one another. To overcome this, the nuclei are shot together at tremendously high speeds. This means that they must be heated to very high temperatures. At a temperature of over one million degrees Celsius, the reaction will work. But to make the process worthwhile, and obtain enough energy, much higher temperatures are needed. The temperature needs to be as high as 400 million degrees Celsius. This is very difficult to produce and control. Scientists are still trying to overcome the problems. Thus, nuclear reactors still use fission to produce energy.

The energy of the stars comes from fusion. The temperatures inside stars are very high. Through a series of chemical reactions, the protons of hydrogen atoms combine to form helium atoms. This releases tremendous amounts of energy. The energy is released as heat and as the light that we see from stars.
D.M.H.W./J.T.

GADOLINIUM (gad′ əl in′ ē əm) Gadolinium is a metallic element. Its chemical symbol is Gd. Its atomic number is 64, and its atomic weight is 157.25. It melts at 1,311°C [2,392°F] and boils at 3,233°C [5,851°F]. Gadolinium is one of the rare earth elements. It is found in the minerals gadolinite, monazite, and cerite. It has seven isotopes.

Gadolinium is used to make control rods for nuclear reactors. It is also used in microwave equipment. Its compounds are used to make phosphors for color television tubes. Gadolinium was discovered by the Swiss chemist Jean de Marignac in 1880. It is named for the Finnish chemist Johan Gadolin.
D.M.H.W./J.R.W.

Yuri Gagarin, a Russian cosmonaut, was the first person to orbit the earth, in spacecraft *Vostok I.*

GAGARIN, YURI ALEKSEYEVICH (1934–1968) Yuri Gagarin (gə ga′ ryin) was the first man to orbit the earth in a spaceship. He was a major in the Soviet Air Force. On April 12, 1961, he was launched in the spacecraft *Vostok 1.* The flight went up to 327 km [203 mi] above the surface of the earth. It made one orbit, which took 1 hour and 48 minutes. The whole spacecraft was 38 m [125 ft] long when it left the launch pad. Most of this was burned up in space. Gagarin returned to earth in a spherical capsule only 228 cm [7½ ft] wide.

Soon after Gagarin's flight, two American astronauts were launched into space. A year later, John Glenn was the first American to go into orbit.

Seven years after his space flight, Gagarin was killed in an airplane crash.   C.M./D.G.F.

GALAXY (gal′ ək sē) A galaxy is a large cluster of stars. Galaxies may also contain gases and large clouds of dust. Most of the stars in a typical galaxy surround a dense cluster of stars that form the nucleus, or core, of the galaxy. Gravitational attraction of the nucleus keeps the stars of a galaxy from flying off into space, and the rotational motion of the galaxy keeps the stars from collapsing into the nucleus.

The total number of galaxies in the universe is unknown. Millions of galaxies have been seen with telescopes, but there may be trillions. The smallest of the known galaxies contains about a million stars. Most galaxies contain billions of stars.

The same gravitational forces that keep the parts of one galaxy together also act to keep groups of galaxies together. Nevertheless, it has been found that all galaxies are moving away from a common point of origin. It has also been found that the more distant galaxies are moving at a higher rate of speed. (*See* RED SHIFT.)

Shapes and sizes The nucleus of a galaxy contains older stars. Younger stars are in the outer areas. There are two main kinds of galaxies: spiral and elliptical. Spiral galaxies are disk-shaped, with a bulging nucleus at the center. Surrounding the disk is a halo of faint, older stars. Galactic halos contain extremely hot interstellar gases. Bands of two or more arms extend in a spiral pattern from the center of the galaxy. Throughout a spiral galaxy are

clouds of dust and gases. Elliptical galaxies are shaped like a globe. Some are round, and some are flattened. Elliptical galaxies have less dust and gases than spiral galaxies do, and they rotate more slowly. A few galaxies

The earth is situated nearer to the edge of the Milky Way galaxy than to the center. No matter which way we look at it from earth, the Milky Way looks like a rather narrow band of stars.

Some of the 100 billion stars of the Milky Way.

are irregular in shape and seem to consist only of young stars.

The size of galaxies is measured in light years because the distance across a galaxy is so great. A light year is the distance light travels in one year. The diameter of a typical spiral galaxy is about 100,000 light years

(5.88 trillion mi; 9.46 trillion km). That means it takes light 100,000 years to travel from one end of the galaxy to the other.

Except for irregular galaxies, a galaxy rotates around an imaginary axis passing through its nucleus. It takes a spiral galaxy about 200 million years to complete one rotation.

Evolution of galaxies The formation of galaxies is thought to have begun with nuclear fusion reactions in earlier generations of massive stars. According to one theory, those reactions threw clouds of hydrogen and helium into space. The elements in such a cloud were gradually recycled until conditions were right for the formation of new stars.

The formation of new stars apparently continues in most galaxies. Dust from dying stars in the galaxy's nucleus is a smoke made up of soot-covered sandy particles. A smoke-cloud of such particles may be several light years in size. Massive interstellar clouds are thought to ''give birth'' to several new stars in one elaborate process. Most galaxies contain thousands of giant rings or patches of star-bearing molecular clouds.

Not all galaxies give off visible light. Some galaxies radiate other kinds of energy. Using the radio telescope, several galaxies that give off strong radio waves but only faint visible light were discovered. Other galaxies give off strong infrared rays, ultraviolet rays, or X rays. (*See* ASTROPHYSICS; OBSERVATORY.)

The Milky Way The sun is one of the stars that make up the galaxy called the Milky Way. The Milky Way is a spiral galaxy that has about two hundred billion stars and is

Top left, The Seyfert Galaxy is a possible intermediate stage between a star and a galaxy. It has a high energy output. Bottom left, a group of spiral galaxies in the constellation *Pegasus*. Top right, an elliptical and a spiral galaxy. Bottom right, a spiral galaxy in the constellation *Ursa Major*.

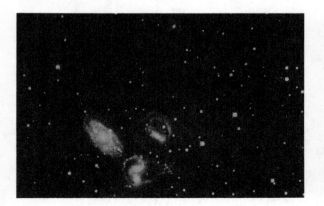

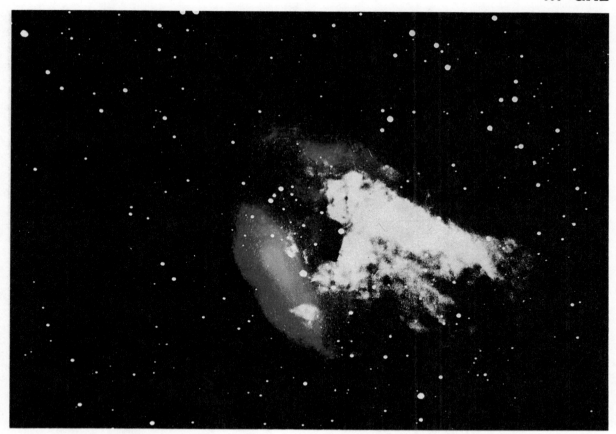

This is the Swan nebula, which is in the constellation Sagittarius. The colored area was created by scientists to show how the nebula would look if viewed through a telescope sensitive to infrared. The colored area is caused by thermal emission of interstellar dust.

about 100,000 light years in diameter.

Observation of the nucleus of the Milky Way using radio and infrared instruments has found it to have a distinct, bright core. It includes a small but very bright body that radiates strong radio waves but whose nature is unknown. The number of stars within 2 light years of its center is thought to be several million.

The spiral disk that makes up the Milky Way is approximately 10,000 light years thick. The sun is located inside the disk and is one of the stars that makes up a spiral arm of the galaxy.

Astronomers can see the Milky Way galaxy only as a rather narrow band of stars. Most stars in the galaxy, including those of the nucleus, are hidden from view by gigantic clouds of dust. The immense number of stars that make up the plane of the disk can sometimes be seen as a faintly glowing band that arches across the night sky from one horizon to the other.

Recent study of the Milky Way by astronomers and chemists indicates that the galaxy is a giant ring of star-bearing molecular clouds, with the sun located on the outer edge of the ring. Within the ring, new stars are always being formed. At the same time, dying stars in the nucleus are supplying new dust clouds to the ring. The sun travels in orbit around the nucleus at a speed of about 155 miles per second (558,000 mph). It completes one orbit in 200 million years.

The Milky Way is one galaxy in a group of galaxies. Of these, the nearest spiral galaxy is the Andromeda galaxy, which is faintly visible to the eye in the Andromeda con-

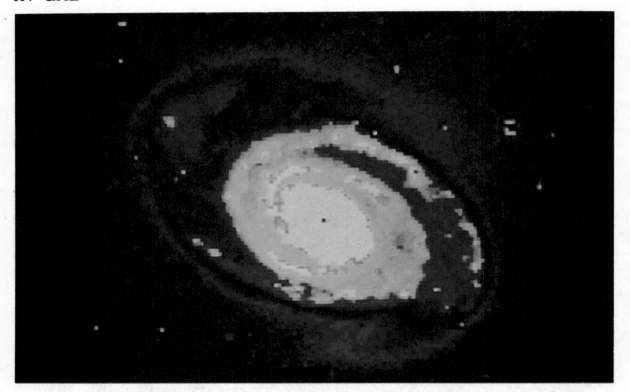

The picture above is a computer-enhanced image of a spiral galaxy in the constellation Virgo. Temperatures are highest in the light-blue areas.

stellation. It is 2 million light years from the Milky Way. It is one-third larger in diameter and has twice as many stars as the Milky Way. Like some other galaxies, Andromeda has a small satellite galaxy orbiting it. The Milky Way has three small, irregular satellite-galaxies, called the Magellanic Clouds.

Astronomers suspect that many stars in the universe have planets, just as the sun does. (*See* EXOBIOLOGY.) If any of the 100 billion other stars have planets, we cannot be sure that any of them would resemble earth. The more we learn about the planets of the sun, the more we see how different they are from earth.

Knowledge of the solar system and of the Milky Way and other galaxies will likely increase dramatically when a space telescope is placed in earth orbit. *See also* OBSERVATORY; SOLAR SYSTEM; STAR.   P.G.Z./G.D.B.

GALEN (A.D. 129–199) Galen (gā′ lən) was a Greek doctor. He was born at Pergamum in Asia Minor. The Roman Empire was large in those days, and Galen studied in Greece, Egypt, and Rome. He was surgeon to the gladiators at Pergamum in A.D. 157. In A.D. 162, he went to Rome. He stayed in Rome and was the personal physician of four emperors before he died.

Galen made many discoveries about medicine and anatomy. One of the things he found out from dissecting animals was that arteries contain blood. He combined his own discoveries with what he had read and learned from other doctors. He wrote hundreds of books, which were used by Arab and European doctors for centuries.

By the time that Galen's books were translated, the Roman Empire had fallen. Christianity was spreading through the world. The Christian Church decided that Galen's ideas were inspired by God. Because of this, his methods were used long after they were out of date.   C.M./D.G.F.

GALENA (gə lē′ nə) Galena is the main ore of lead. It is a soft, heavy, metallic gray mineral. Galena is a lead sulfide. Its chemical formula is PbS. Sulfides are mineral which contain sulfur in combination with metals. By weight, galena is 87% lead and 13% sulfur. It is commonly found in masses in limestone or in veins of minerals, also containing sulfides of iron, zinc, and copper. Some deposits of galena contain silver and are refined to obtain both lead and silver. The chief sources of galena are Canada, Australia, Germany, Mexico, the Soviet Union, and the United States. J.J.A./R.H.

Galileo discovered the law that describes the time of the swing of a pendulum. He applied it to the design of a clock that was an improvement over existing clocks. This is a model of it.

GALILEO (1564-1642) Galileo (gä′ lə lē′ ō) is the name commonly used for Galileo Galilei, an Italian physicist. He was one of the first scientists to use modern scientific methods. He lived in an age when the Catholic Church was very powerful. The Church thought that science was a threat to the ideas of Christianity. Galileo's work brought him into conflict with the Church.

Galileo studied at the University of Pisa. While he was in the cathedral there, he made his first discovery. He saw that the hanging lights swung steadily from side to side in the draft. He did experiments to show that this movement was regular enough for measuring time. This discovery was used 60 years later in making clocks with pendulums. Galileo became professor of mathematics at Pisa. He is supposed to have proved his ideas about gravity by dropping different weights from the top of the Leaning Tower. His beliefs were against the ideas of Aristotle, and Galileo had to leave the university.

Galileo went to Padua in 1592 and began

Galileo is believed to have been the first to suggest that gravity pulls all objects to the ground with the same acceleration. According to legend, Galileo simultaneously dropped a one-pound and a ten-pound weight from the Leaning Tower of Pisa. Both weights struck the ground at about the same instant. This proved Galileo's theory to be correct.

work on a telescope. With it, he discovered mountains and craters on the moon and saw for the first time the four largest moons of Jupiter. His discoveries led him to believe that the earth and planets move around the sun, as Copernicus had said. But the Church wanted to believe that the sun moved around the earth. Galileo was accused of heresy by the Inquisition. He would not deny what he had seen. He was found guilty and was imprisoned in a house in Florence for the rest of his life. In 1984, the Church formally acknowledged that it had erred in condemning him. *See also* ARISTOTLE; COPERNICUS.

C.M./D.G.F.

GALLBLADDER (gòl′ blad′ ər) The gallbladder is a small baglike organ inside the body, lying close to the liver. It is found in most animals with a backbone, including humans. It stores a greenish yellow fluid called bile. Bile is produced by the liver and flows into the gallbladder. Bile contains special chemicals that help to break down fatty foods in the small intestine. (*See* DIGESTION.) A special chemical, called a hormone, makes the gallbladder release the bile into the small intestine as soon as food passes into it from the stomach.

Gallstones may sometimes form in the gallbladder. These are hard pebblelike lumps that can cause pain and give rise to jaundice. They can be removed by a surgeon, although often the entire gallbladder has to be removed.

J.A./J.J.F.

GALLIUM (gal′ ē əm) Gallium is a gray, shiny metallic element. Its chemical symbol is Ga. Its atomic number is 31, and its atomic weight is 69.72. Its melting point is 30°C [86°F] and its boiling point is 2,403°C [4,357°F]. It is found in the mineral germanite and also in zinc blende.

Gallium is used to make alloys with aluminum and other metals. Gallium arsenide is used to make transistors. Its low melting point and high boiling point make it suitable for use in high-temperature thermometers. Gallium was discovered by the French chemist Lecoq de Boisbaudran in 1875.

D.M.H.W./J.R.W.

GALL WASP (gòl wäsp) Gall wasps are any of about 750 species of insects belonging to the family Cynipidae. They lay their eggs just under the surface of plants. When the eggs are

One member of the 750 species of gall wasps. The female gall wasp lays her eggs in plant tissues; and, as the grub develops, its secretions cause the surrounding tissues to grow into a gall. Some galls contain just one grub, but others may have several.

laid or when these eggs hatch into larvae, they cause the plant tissue to swell, forming galls. Although the exact reason for the formation of galls is not known, it is believed that the mother or the larvae release a chemical. This chemical causes the plant tissue in the area to grow abnormally, forming a gall.

Inside the gall, one or more larvae feed on the plant tissue as they prepare to change into pupae which develop into adults. (*See* METAMORPHOSIS.) Although these parasites cause some damage, they rarely kill a plant. Some gall wasps lay their eggs in galls occupied by other insects. Each species of gall wasp produces a characteristic type of gall on a specific type of plant. Although oak trees are a favorite of many gall wasps, some species prefer to attack members of the rose family and composite family.

Gall wasps are tiny, rarely growing more than 8 mm [0.25 in] long. Most are dark brown or black and have a shiny abdomen flattened on the sides. Reproduction is frequently by parthenogenesis, or the development of unfertilized eggs. As a result, male gall wasps are rare. Some species alternate this parthenogenetic stage with a sexually reproductive stage. (*See* ALTERNATION OF GENERATIONS.)

Galls can also be caused by some species of flies, aphids, bugs, beetles, moths, and mites. The galls are often preyed upon by birds, insects, and squirrels. These predators eat the larvae after ripping open the gall. Some gall wasp larvae produce a bad-tasting fluid that discourages predators. *See also* ICHNEUMON FLY.   A.J.C./J.E.R.

GALVANI, LUIGI (1737–1798) Luigi Galvani (gäl vä′ nē) was an Italian doctor. He is most famous for his discovery of the connection between electricity and muscle movements.

Galvani used frogs' legs for his experiments. He arranged a copper wire so that it touched a leg muscle and a silver wire so that it touched a nerve. When the other ends of the wires were touched together, the leg muscle twitched. Galvani thought that the muscle and nerve tissue had made an electric current. He was wrong about this. (*See* CELL, ELECTRICAL.) But his discovery made it possible for other scientists to investigate the role of electricity in living tissue.   C.M./D.G.F.

Luigi Galvani, left, was born in Bologna. He studied and practiced medicine there. His discovery that a muscle could be made to contract by applying an electric current to it laid the foundation for the study of electricity and of neurophysiology.

GALVANIZING (gal′ və nī′ zing) Galvanizing is the process of coating an article with a layer of zinc. Only articles made of steel or iron are galvanized. Galvanizing protects the steel or iron from corrosion by the atmosphere. If the steel or iron is unprotected, it becomes corroded and rust forms. The zinc coating prevents this from happening. Even if the coating wears away at some point, the metal beneath does not corrode. The zinc coating surrounding the corrosion is attacked instead. A great many articles are galvanized, including buckets, electricity pylons, and chicken wire. About half of all the zinc mined is used for galvanizing.

There are several methods for coating an article with zinc. Sometimes the article is dipped in molten zinc. The article is first treated to remove grease. Then it is pickled in acid. This removes the rust. Then it is treated with a flux. The flux helps the zinc to cling to the surface of the article. Usually a small amount of aluminum is added to the molten zinc. This helps the zinc to flow over the surface of the article.

Another common method of galvanizing is by electroplating. In this process, the article is placed in a solution of a zinc salt, along with some zinc. An electric current is passed through the solution from the article to the zinc. The current causes the zinc to dissolve in the solution. The zinc comes out of the solution at the article, where it is deposited. Alternatively, the zinc can be sprayed onto the article by a metallization pistol. This pistol contains molten zinc which is sprayed out as a very fine mist. In sherardizing, the article is tumbled inside a barrel with zinc dust. The zinc penetrates through the surface of the article. It forms an alloy with the iron inside the surface and forms a coating over the surface. *See also* ELECTROPLATING.   M.E./A.D.

Galvanizing metal products protects them from corrosion. Here, window frames are being galvanized by the hot dip method.

GALVANOMETER (gal′ və näm′ ət ər) A galvanometer is a delicate scientific instrument. It is used to detect electric current and measure its strength. It is named for the Italian physician Luigi Galvani, who experimented with electricity in the 18th century.

A galvanometer detects the magnetic field that an electric current produces. A wire carrying electricity behaves like a magnet. It attracts or repels another magnet. If we measure how strongly the magnets pull or push, this shows how strong the electric current is. One kind of galvanometer has a coil of wire to carry the current. It is suspended between the poles of a permanent magnet. When electricity flows round the coil, the coil becomes magnetic. It twists around between the poles of the magnet. A mirror is attached to the coil. A beam of light is arranged to fall on the mirror. It is reflected along a scale. Every time the coil moves, the spot of light moves too.

When a strong current is passing through the coil, the coil is strongly twisted. It produces a high reading on the scale. If the current is passed in the opposite direction, the coil twists in the opposite direction, too. So the galvanometer can be used to tell which direction a current is flowing, as well as how

When an electric current flows into a galvanometer, a coil inside the instrument produces a small magnetic field. This field interacts with the stronger magnetic field of a permanent magnet, and the coil is deflected. When this happens, a mirror that is attached to the coil reflects a beam of light onto a scale. By reading this scale, the operator can measure the strength of the electric current.

strong it is. The scale may be calibrated to show voltage and current. (*See* CALIBRATION.) *See also* AMMETER; VOLTMETER.

D.M.H.W./R.W.L.

GAMETE (gə mēt′) A gamete, or germ cell, is a mature sex cell. In plants, male gametes are called pollen grains. In animals, male gametes are called sperm. The female gametes in plants and animals are called eggs or ova. A male gamete and a female gamete join during fertilization to form a zygote. This is part of sexual reproduction.

In most plants and animals, gametes are formed by meiosis. (*See* MEIOSIS.) During meiosis, each gamete receives one of the two sets of chromosomes found in all other body cells. Gametes, therefore, are haploid, and have chromosome number N. When two gametes combine, the zygote gets one set of chromosomes from each gamete. Thus, the zygote has two sets, or the normal number of chromosomes, 2N. This is said to be diploid. *See also* EMBRYO; FERTILIZATION; HEREDITY; REPRODUCTION.

A.J.C./E.R.L.

GAMMA RAY (gam′ ə rā) A gamma ray is a high energy electromagnetic ray of very short wavelength, similar to X rays. Gamma rays are produced during the breaking down of the atoms of radioactive elements.

Members of the uranium-radium series of radioactive elements give off gamma rays when they disintegrate to form new elements. (*See* RADIOACTIVE SERIES.)

When gamma rays pass through the human body, they ionize, or give electric charges to some of the body's tissue. This ionization sometimes destroys cells. Extremely small amounts of gamma rays bombard us from the natural activity of the things around us, such as from the water we drink and the air we breathe. Large amounts of gamma rays are dangerous. But they can also be of benefit. They may be used to treat some cancers, tumors, and skin problems. With X-ray machines, medical experts use gamma rays to examine the body for broken bones, foreign objects, and for signs of disease.

J.J.A./J.T.

GANNET (gan′ ət) Gannets are white and black seabirds that belong to the family Sulidae. They are 77.5 cm [31 in] long with a wingspan of 175 cm [70 in]. There are three species in the world: one near Australia, one near South Africa, and one in the North Atlantic. In the winter, gannets stay out in the open ocean, catching fish by diving into the water from heights of 15 m [50 ft]. In the summer, the birds nest in large numbers on islands.

S.R.G./M.L.

GAR (gär) The gar is a primitive freshwater fish that belongs to the family Lepisosteidae. There are five species found throughout central and much of eastern North America. The gars are long, slender fish with narrow snouts and many sharp teeth. The alligator gar may reach lengths of 2.8 m [9 ft]. Gars eat other fish and are often considered a nuisance fish. They lie very still in the water and dash out to eat any fish that swims past. In some parts of the South—particularly in Louisiana —fishing for gar is a popular sport.

S.R.G./E.C.M.

GARLIC (gär′ lik) Garlic (*Allium sativum*) is a perennial plant belonging to the lily family. It is closely related to the onion. Garlic is native to Europe and Asia. It is now cultivated throughout the world and used to flavor food. Garlic produces two types of bulbs or bulblets. The aerial bulblets produced on the flower stalk are used to start new plants. The underground bulbs, called cloves, are the ones sold in stores. They are formed at the base of the plant much like an onion.

In ancient times, garlic was used as a good luck charm and as a drug. Its value as a medicine has been confirmed as garlic contains allium. Allium is an antibiotic that can also be used as an antiseptic. A.J.C./F.W.S.

GARNET (gär′ nət) Garnets represent a group of minerals. There are some semi-precious garnets used for jewelry, especially the ruby-red pyrope and the transparent almandine garnet. Some garnets are used as abrasives.

Garnets are found in South Africa, Arizona, and Colorado. The garnet is the birthstone of January.   J.M.C./W.R.S.

Several large garnets are shown in the photograph above.

GARTER SNAKE (gärt′ ər snāk) A garter snake is a medium sized snake that belongs to the family Colubridae. There are eight different species of garter snakes in North America. Although some species are found only in certain areas, the eight species together are found throughout the United States. Garter snakes are very common in many areas of the country. They are often found near water. Most species grow to 66 cm [26 in] in length. Garter snakes were so named because their colorful lines resembled fancy garter straps once used to hold up gentlemen's socks. Garter snakes eat frogs, toads, insects, and small mammals and birds.   S.R.G./R.L.L.

GAS (gas) Gas, liquid, and solid are the three states of matter. In a solid, the atoms or molecules are fixed in position. In a liquid, they are free to move within limits. In a gas, the atoms or molecules are able to move wherever they can. A gas fills whatever it is put into and takes the container's shape. A gas without any container would just go on and on expanding. On the other hand, a gas can be squeezed into a smaller and smaller container. This cannot happen with liquids or solids. They have molecules with much less freedom.

The molecules of a gas are in constant motion. They move without stopping. They bounce off each other, and they bounce off the walls of their container. As they bombard the walls, they press against them. The pressure of a gas is due to the momentum of all the molecules hitting against their container walls. The behavior of gases is explained if we think of them as molecules in constant motion. This is called the kinetic theory of gases. Kinetic means ''having to do with movement.''

If a gas is squeezed into a smaller and smaller space, the molecules have less room to move around. They hit the walls more and more often. The pressure goes up. When a certain point is reached, the molecules can hardly move at all. The gas turns into a liquid. The same thing happens when a gas is cooled. When a gas is cooled, energy is taken from its molecules. They slow down and do not bounce off each other as vigorously. They get closer and closer and turn into a liquid.

Some gases can be turned into liquids just by compressing them. But many need to be cooled as well. There is a temperature for each gas, called the critical temperature. Above this, it is impossible to liquefy the gas. The critical temperature for the gas ammonia is 132°C [270°F]. Above this temperature it cannot be turned into a liquid. The critical temperature for nitrogen is much lower. It must be cooled to −147°C [−233°F] before liquid nitrogen is made. The critical temperature for hydrogen is −240°C [−400°F], and for helium it is even lower, −268°C [−450°F]. This is getting near the lowest temperature possible, which is −273°C [−459°F].

To reach very low temperatures, special

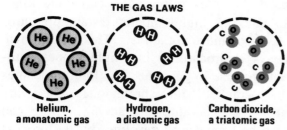

THE GAS LAWS

Helium, a monatomic gas

Hydrogen, a diatomic gas

Carbon dioxide, a triatomic gas

Avogadro's law: *Equal volumes of gases at the same temperature and pressure contain equal numbers of molecules.* From the law, it can be shown that the molecular weight in grams of any gas at 0°C and one atmosphere pressure will occupy a volume of 22.4 liters.

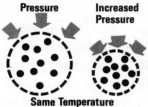

Pressure

Increased Pressure

Same Temperature

Boyle's law: *The volume of a gas at constant temperature varies inversely with pressure.* In practice, this law is only an approximation. It does not apply exactly to most gases.

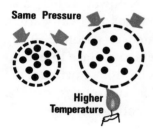

Same Pressure

Higher Temperature

Charles' law: *The volume of a gas at constant pressure varies directly with absolute temperature.* The volume of a gas will increase by 1/273 for each °C increase.

Graham's law: *Gases diffuse at rates inversely proportional to the square roots of their densities.* This diagram illustrates Graham's law.

Gas of Density = 1

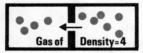

Gas of Density = 4

Chlorine gas is made in the laboratory by heating manganese dioxide with concentrated hydrochloric acid. The chlorine is collected over water.

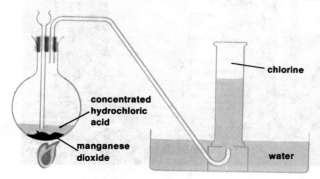

chlorine

concentrated hydrochloric acid

manganese dioxide

water

cooling methods must be used. Nitrogen cannot be liquefied by normal refrigeration. Instead, it is cooled as far as possible and then compressed. Then the compressed gas is allowed to expand through a nozzle. This causes cooling by the Joule-Thomson effect. The temperature falls below the critical temperature and the nitrogen liquefies. This method will not work with hydrogen. Hydrogen is liquefied by evaporating liquid air. This produces sufficient cooling.

The Irish scientist Robert Boyle discovered the important law about gases that is called after him. (*See* BOYLE'S LAW.) It states that the volume of a gas will increase as its pressure decreases, and vice versa. The French scientist Jacques Charles stated another important law a century later. (*See* CHARLES' LAW.) Charles' law states that the volume a gas occupies under constant pressure varies with its temperature.

Gases have very low densities. This explains why they are poor conductors of heat and electricity. For an electric current to pass through a centimeter of dry air, a voltage of about 30,000 volts must be applied to the gap. This causes ions to form.

Eleven of the elements are gases at room temperature. These are hydrogen, nitrogen, oxygen, fluorine, and chlorine, and the six noble gases helium, neon, argon, krypton, xenon, and radon. Pairs of atoms of the first five combine to form molecules. The molecule of oxygen can thus be written O_2, and the molecule of hydrogen H_2. They are diatomic gases. The atoms of noble gases do not form molecules. They are monatomic gases. Air is not a single gas. It is a mixture of gases, mainly nitrogen and oxygen.

D.M.H.W./J.R.W.

GAS METER (gas′ mēt′ ər) A gas meter is a device with dials and pointers that tells how much gas has been used. Usually, the gas meter is a metal box divided through the center into two main chambers. Each chamber has a movable wall called a partition. These partitions divide each chamber into two parts, making a total of four separate chambers.

The gas is measured by first filling and then emptying each of these four chambers. The number of times each chamber is filled and emptied is automatically registered. The volume of each chamber is fixed and tested. While one chamber is being filled, another is being emptied. The consumer receives an even flow of gas at all times.

The upper part of the gas meter contains the instrument that registers the movement of the various chambers. The volume, either in cubic feet or cubic meters, is shown on a set of dials. J.J.A./R.W.L.

GASOLINE (gas′ ə lēn′) Gasoline is a thin, highly flammable liquid. It is a mixture of many different hydrocarbons. It is obtained from petroleum by distillation. It readily turns to vapor, and is explosive when mixed with air. This makes it an ideal fuel for automobile engines.

When petroleum is distilled, it gives only about 25% gasoline. The gasoline is not very good quality. To get high quality, or grade, gasoline from petroleum, other processes are used. The most important is called cracking. In cracking, high temperatures and pressures are used, and also catalysts. This breaks down heavy hydrocarbons into lighter ones, suitable for use in gasoline. The long molecules are "cracked" into shorter ones. Gases are also produced during cracking. These can also be turned into gasoline, by the process called polymerization. There are several other processes that can be carried out on the petroleum products obtained by distillation. The final yield is over 50% high-grade gasoline from petroleum.

In a gasoline engine, gasoline is mixed with air. The mixture is exploded in the automobile's cylinders. This drives the pistons. If the mixture explodes too quickly, a noise called knocking, or pinging, is heard in the engine. The engine loses power. It may also be damaged. Certain kinds of hydrocarbon called octanes are found in gasoline. They determine the gasoline's resistance to knocking. The higher the proportion of octanes, the less knocking there is. Gasolines can be graded by their octane rating.

A gasoline refinery in Texas. At such refineries, crude oil is separated into light gases, gas oils, and gasoline, which is further distilled into grades.

Several substances called additives may be put into gasoline to improve it. Lead tetraethyl acts as an antiknock agent. Other additives prevent oxidation in the fuel storage tank. Some prevent harmful material from the gasoline, such as lead, from being deposited in the engine. Some additives act as lubricants. They reduce the friction between the pistons and the engine cylinders.

D.M.H.W./J.M.

GASTROCNEMIUS (gas′ träk nē′ mē əs) The gastrocnemius is a large powerful muscle at the back of the lower half of the leg. This part of the leg is called the calf. The gastrocnemius is attached at one end to the lower end of the upper leg bone (femur) and at the other to a bone in the heel. When the gastrocnemius gets shorter, or contracts, it pulls the heel up from the ground. This action serves to push the whole body forward during walking and running. Many muscles work with the gastrocnemius to produce movement. *See also* HAMSTRING.

J.A./J.J.F.

GASTROPOD (gas′ trə päd′) Gastropods compose a class of mollusks that include snails and slugs. Gastropods are often called univalves, meaning "one shell." Most gastropods have only one shell, although there are some gastropods with no shell at all.

Gastropods move by means of a single, large foot. In many gastropods, there is a horny plate called an operculum at the back of the foot. When in danger, the operculum closes the shell opening, allowing the gastropod to hide inside. Most land gastropods have no operculum.

Most of the gastropods' internal organs are located in the visceral hump. This hump always remains within the shell. Except for the sea slugs, marine and freshwater gastropods breathe by means of gills, located in a space called the mantle cavity. In land snails, the mantle cavity has changed into a lung. A few gastropods have lungs, although they live

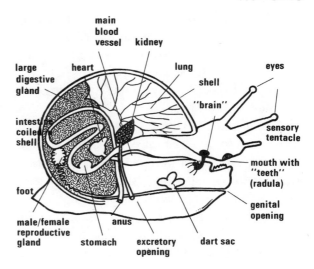

Above, diagram of the structure of a land snail. This gastropod is hermaphrodite—that is, it produces both female and male sex cells. It exchanges sperm cells with another snail. Land snails are vegetarian. Below, the white dog whelk, a carnivorous marine gastropod. Notice that its eyes are at the base of the tentacles.

in the water. In this case, they must come up to the water surface to breathe.

Some types of gastropods have two pairs of tentacles, or feelers. One pair is used by the gastropod to feel its way about. Eyes are often attached to the other pair.

Gastropods eat by means of a radula. A radula is a tonguelike mass of tissue covered by teeth. In vegetarian gastropods, the teeth are numerous but weak. In carnivorous gastropods, there are several dozen strong teeth.

Most gastropods have separate sexes, but some of the lung-breathing snails are hermaphrodites. This means that each animal has separate male and female sex organs. (*See* HERMAPHRODITE.)

Gastropods are mainly sea animals. They include not only slugs and snails, but whelks, winkles, and limpets as well.   J.M.C./R.J.B.

GAS TURBINE (gas′ tər′ bən) A gas turbine is a kind of internal-combustion engine. Basically, a turbine is a wheel that is turned by the force of a moving fluid. The turning wheel is mounted on a shaft, and the shaft in

turn powers a machine—such as an airplane or ship engine, a locomotive engine, or an electric generator. (*See also* TURBINE.)

A gas turbine can use almost any kind of fuel that gives off gases when burned. Natural gas, oil, and kerosene are usually used in gas turbines. The important difference between a steam turbine and a gas turbine is that in a steam turbine the energy from the burning fuel must first heat water in order to create steam, which then turns the turbine wheel. In a gas turbine, the energy from the burning fuel turns the turbine wheel directly.

The three main parts of a gas turbine are the compressor, the combustion chamber, and the turbine wheel.

The compressor does two things. First, it sucks in air from the outside, and then it compresses the air. The compressed air next passes into the combustion chamber and mixes with the fuel. The mixture of com-

Below, the Rolls Royce Dart Turboprop engine, cut away to show its many parts. Air is drawn into the front of the engine and into the compressor. Fuel is mixed with the air and ignited in the combustion chamber. Exhaust gases turn the propeller.

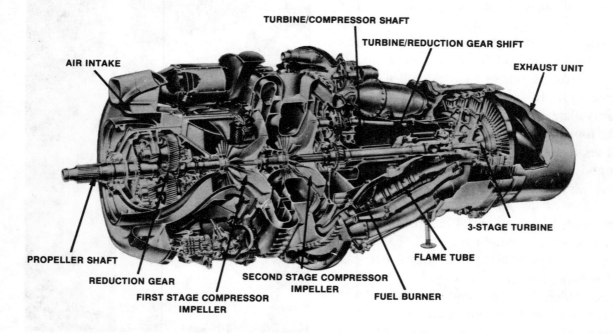

TURBINE/COMPRESSOR SHAFT

TURBINE/REDUCTION GEAR SHIFT

AIR INTAKE

EXHAUST UNIT

3-STAGE TURBINE

PROPELLER SHAFT

FLAME TUBE

REDUCTION GEAR

SECOND STAGE COMPRESSOR IMPELLER

FUEL BURNER

FIRST STAGE COMPRESSOR IMPELLER

The business jet above is powered by a gas turbine.

pressed air and fuel is then ignited by an electric spark. The compressed, burning gases expand with tremendous force, and as they rush from the combustion chamber, they pass through the blades of the turbine wheel and turn it. The wheel is connected to a shaft, and the turning shaft then powers some device.

After the gases pass the turbine wheel, they escape through the exhaust. These exhaust gases can be used to help operate the turbine. In some gas turbines—such as those used to run an electric generator—the exhaust is used to heat the air in the compressor. That means that less fuel is needed to burn the gas in the combustion chamber, which means that the turbine is more efficient. In other gas turbines—such as those used in aircraft engines—the exhaust gases are forced out of the back of the engine. This creates more forward power for the airplane.

Steam and water turbines have been in use since about 1900. Gas turbines, however, could not be built until metal alloys could be developed to withstand the heat created in the combustion chamber. Engineers perfected the gas turbine in the early 1940s. Today gas turbines are used to power land, sea, and air vehicles; in industry; and in electric-power plants.

The widest use of gas turbines is in jet-aircraft engines. Gas turbines are most efficient when they operate at full power. So they are well-suited to high-speed jet aircraft. Gas turbines are also used in turbo-prop engines. In a turbo-prop engine, the gas turbine powers the propeller. In addition, however, the exhaust gases are forced out of the back of the engine, which adds to the thrust of the engine. (*See also* JET PROPULSION.) Another use of the gas turbine in aircraft is in turbofan engines. The turbofan engine works much like a conventional jet engine, but there is a fan placed where the outside air enters the engine. The fan takes in much more air, and it also compresses the air. Most of this compressed air travels around the engine through a bypass duct. The air exits the engine at a greater speed than it had when it entered. This gives the engine extra forward power.

During the 1950s gas turbines were used in some railroad locomotives. However, gas-turbine engines are less efficient than the diesel engines used in most locomotives.

Because of the relatively small size and light weight of gas turbine engines, they were adapted to use in ships in the early 1970s.

Beginning in the 1960s and continuing into the 1980s experiments were made in using gas turbines in automotive vehicles. However, cost of manufacturing and operation has prevented gas turbines from replacing the regular internal-combustion engine in cars and trucks.

Two applications of the gas turbine in industry are in the oil refining process and in compressor stations along natural-gas pipelines.

Most turbines in electric-power stations are steam turbines. That is because the pressure of a gas turbine is not great enough to operate a whole power plant. However, gas turbines are often used along with steam turbines to increase the efficiency of a plant.

Gas turbines are also used as a standby system and for portable electric-power plants.

S.K.L./G.D.B.

GAUSS (gaùs) The gauss is a unit used to measure the strength of a magnetic field. It is named after Karl F. Gauss, a German mathematician, who did important work in electromagnetism.

The magnetic field of the earth measures about one half a gauss. It is believed that the magnetic field at the surface of a neutron star or pulsar may be as large as several billion gauss. Special superconducting magnets now being developed can produce magnetic fields of 50,000 gauss or more. *See also* ELECTROMAGNETISM; GAUSS, KARL. J.J.A./R.W.L.

GAUSS, KARL FRIEDRICH (1777–1855) Karl Gauss (gaùs) was a German mathematician. He was born at Brunswick, the son of a poor gardener. He was so brilliant that Duke Ferdinand noticed him and paid for his education.

Gauss was very interested in numbers. He made his first great discovery in geometry when he was a student. Using only a straightedge and compasses, he worked out how to make a 17-sided polygon. Even the ancient Greek mathematicians had not managed to do this. He went on to prove that some polygons could never be drawn with only a straightedge and compasses. This was the first time anyone had proved something in geometry to be impossible. After that, proving that things were impossible became an important field of mathematics.

Gauss also became famous as an astronomer. He invented a machine called a heliotrope. This reflected sunlight over long distances. He used the straight lines of reflected light to measure the shape of the earth by trigonometry.

Gauss studied magnetism. He worked out the positions of the earth's magnetic poles. He needed a set of units to measure magnetic effects. He worked these out in 1832. At the same time, he made a study of the theory of measurement. The unit of magnetic flux density is named for him. (*See* GAUSS.) There is a statue of Gauss in Brunswick. It is mounted on a 17-pointed star.   C.M./D.G.F.

GAVIAL (gav′ ē əl) A gavial is a reptile that belongs to the family Gavialidae. It is related to alligators and crocodiles, but is quite different in appearance. Gavials sometimes grow as long as 6.6 m [20 ft], and have a long, slender snout. Unlike some of the alligators and crocodiles, the gavial is not dangerous to humans because it only eats fish. It lives only in a few rivers in India.   S.R.G./R.L.L.

Joseph Louis Gay-Lussac was born in St. Leonard-de-Noblet in 1778. He is noted for his work on the chemistry of gases. He also improved the processes for making sulfuric acid and oxalic acid for use in industry. This early chemist also found a way to determine the alkalinity of soda and potash.

GAY-LUSSAC, JOSEPH (1778–1850) Joseph Gay-Lussac (gā′ lü sak′) was a French chemist. He made many important discoveries. The most famous of these is the way in which gases expand when they are warmed. Gay-Lussac found out in 1802 that all gases expand equally when they are given the same change in temperature. He discovered that the volume of any gas is proportional to the absolute temperature. This was discovered at the same time by Jacques Charles and is called Charles' Law

One volume of oxygen combines with two volumes of hydrogen to give water. Gay-Lussac discovered this and showed how a law could be derived from this that applied to other substances made from gases. He called this the law of combining volumes.

Gay-Lussac also worked on acids and alkalis. He was interested in the practical use of his discoveries. As well as being a professor, he worked on government committees. *See also* CHARLES' LAW.   C.M./D.G.F.

GAZELLE (gə zel′) The gazelle is any of about 12 species of slender, graceful antelopes belonging to the genus *Gazella*. These mammals are herbivores and belong to the same family (Bovidae) as cattle. They roam the plains of Africa and Asia in herds of 5 to 200. Most gazelles stand about 90 cm [3 ft] tall at the shoulder, and have large black eyes, and long, pointed ears. They are light to dark brown with a white belly and a small white tail. With the exception of the female Persian gazelle (*Gazella subgutturosa*), both sexes have long, slightly curved horns. The horns of most species are ringed.

Grant's gazelles feeding on scrub vegetation in Kenya, Africa. This species has the largest horns of all of the gazelles. Like other gazelles, it is admired for its grace and speed.

The most common gazelles are Thomson's gazelle (*Gazella thomsoni*) and Grant's gazelle (*Gazella granti*). The name "gazelle" comes from an Arabic word meaning "affectionate."

Gazelles are fast runners and often reach speeds of 65 km [40 mi] per hour. Gazelles are protected by law in most countries. Because of extensive illegal hunting, however, some species of gazelles are endangered and may soon be extinct.   A.J.C./J.J.M.

GEAR (gir) A gear is a mechanical device that transfers power and rotating motion from one part of a machine to another. One of the most common gears is the spur gear. It consists of a metal wheel with slots, called teeth, around the edge. The teeth of one gear are fitted into the teeth of another gear. Thus, when the first gear turns, the second gear turns with it. The gears are mounted on shafts, called axles. One axle runs to the source of power. When the power axle turns, its gear turns. This causes the second gear to turn, which makes the second axle rotate.

When gears are disconnected, the machine is said to be out of gear. Automobiles, for example, are put out of gear by moving the gear shift lever to a neutral position. This action causes the gears to move apart, and the automobile does not move even though its engine is running.

Gears usually operate in pairs. Generally, one gear is larger than the other gear. They are known respectively as gear and pinion. If the pinion, or smaller gear, is the driving member, the system acts as a speed reducer. This is because the larger gear that supplies the power to the machine turns more slowly than the small gear that is driving it. But if the gear drives the pinion, the system acts as a speed increaser. Now, the small gear, or pinion, supplies power to the machine. It turns at a faster speed than the large gear. For example, a 30-tooth gear driving a 15-tooth pinion doubles the speed of the pinion. The gear ratio is said to be 2 to 1. This system also doubles the power. This is how an automobile in low gear generates the power to start the car moving from a standing start.

Gear and pinion turn in opposite directions when they mesh, or come together.

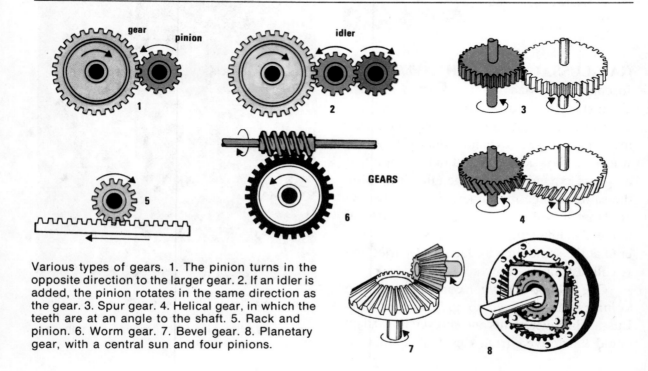

Various types of gears. 1. The pinion turns in the opposite direction to the larger gear. 2. If an idler is added, the pinion rotates in the same direction as the gear. 3. Spur gear. 4. Helical gear, in which the teeth are at an angle to the shaft. 5. Rack and pinion. 6. Worm gear. 7. Bevel gear. 8. Planetary gear, with a central sun and four pinions.

Geckos are lizards that have short, flat bodies. The pads of their toes are covered with many tiny hooks, which allow geckos to cling firmly to surfaces, even to glass. Most geckos come out at night to feed, mostly on insects.

However, if it is necessary for them both to turn in the same direction, a third gear, called an idler, is positioned between them. This arrangement is called a compound train of gears.

Another type of gear arrangement is called the rack and pinion system. This is used in automobile steering systems and in microscope focusing mechanisms. The rack is usually a straight piece of metal with teeth. The teeth on the pinion mesh with the teeth on the rack and cause it to move in a straight line in either direction.

Other types of gears include bevel gears, worm gears, helical gears, friction gears, and planetary gears. Bevel gears have teeth that slant at angles. They usually transfer power at right angles. Worm gears have one gear similar to a spur gear, and an endless screw around one of the axles. The teeth in the spur gear mesh with the screw, and cause it to turn the second shaft. Helical gears resemble spur gears, but their teeth run at an angle to the shaft, not parallel to it. Helical gears are sometimes called spiral gears.

Friction gears do not have teeth. Instead, they use a shaft-driven wheel that presses against another wheel. Friction gears do not provide as much power as toothed gears. Automobile transmissions use planetary gear systems. The system consists of planetary, or pinion, gears that rotate around a sun, or central gear, in much the same way the planets of the solar system rotate around the sun. *See also* AUTOMOBILE; DIFFERENTIAL.

W.R.P./J.T.

GECKO (gek′ ō) A gecko is a lizard that belongs to the family Gekkonidae. It gets its name from the sound it makes. Geckos have thousands of little bristles like suction cups on their toes. These bristles allow the lizard to climb and cling to smooth rocks, trees, and even glass. The major food of a gecko is insects. This group of lizards is found all over the world in tropical and subtropical climates. They are often found around houses and docks, where they are mistakenly brought aboard ships. The geckos' habit of living on ships has resulted in their being taken all over the world. Five of the eight species of geckos in the United States were originally from other lands but were carried to the United States by ships. S.R.G./R.L.L.

GEIGER COUNTER (gī′ gər kaùnt′ ər) The Geiger counter, also called the Geiger-Müller counter, is a device used to record and measure the presence of radioactivity. Geiger counters in use today are based on designs made by the German physicists Hans Geiger and W. Müller in the 1920s.

The Geiger counter is usually made in the form of a thin metal cylinder enclosed in a glass tube. The tube is made in a wide range of shapes and sizes. A thin wire comes down through the middle of the cylinder. This central wire and the inner wall of the cylinder are connected to an electricity supply. The wire becomes a positive electrode. The metal wall of the cylinder serves as a negative electrode.

If ionizing radiation, such as alpha particles, beta particles, gamma rays, or X rays, is sent into the cylinder, the air or other gas inside becomes ionized (charged). (*See* IONS AND IONIZATION.)

These ions cause an electric spark to jump from the wire to the cylinder, producing a short pulse of current. These pulses are then counted electronically. The rate of the pulse activity indicates the strength of the radioactivity. This can be read on a meter. In addition, the pulses are usually amplified (increased) and fed to a small loudspeaker in the instrument. (*See* AMPLIFIER.) The pulses can then be heard as a series of clicks.

Besides locating sources of radioactivity, Geiger counters are sometimes used with other devices to uncover flaws (imperfections) in case metals and to measure the thickness of sheet materials.

Some uranium prospectors carry small Geiger counters as standard equipment. Because large Geiger counters are too big and clumsy to be used in the field, a smaller device, the scintillation counter, is often used instead for survey work. The scintillation counter has also replaced the Geiger counter in scientific research. A scintillation counter can measure low-level radioactivity more efficiently. J.J.A./R.W.L.

GEMINI (jem′ ə nē) Gemini is a zodiac constellation that lies between Cancer and Taurus. Its two brightest stars are Castor and Pollux. The sun is in Gemini during the summer solstice, which marks the beginning of summer in the northern hemisphere. The shape of the constellation is said to represent twin brothers. J.M.C./C.R.

GENE (jēn) A gene is a unit of heredity. It determines characteristics that an organism inherits from its parents. Each gene influences one particular characteristic, but it may take hundreds of genes to determine completely that characteristic.

Genes are located on chromosomes in the nucleus of a cell. (*See* CHROMOSOME.) Each cell contains thousands of genes. Each of these genes has a specific location on one of the chromosomes. This location is called a locus.

Genes control heredity by controlling the formation of enzymes within the cell. (*See* ENZYME.) Therefore, they also control all the chemical and physical processes that take place in the development of that cell. (*See* CELLULAR DIFFERENTIATION.) Genes are made of DNA. DNA carries the code for inheritance. The genes of some viruses are made of RNA. *See also* HEREDITY; MEIOSIS; MITOSIS; MUTATION. A.J.C./E.R.C.

GENERATOR, ELECTRICAL An electrical generator (jen′ ə rāt′ ər) is a machine that produces electricity. Electricity is a form of energy. A generator converts movement, another form of energy, into electrical energy. It does this by making use of a relationship between electricity and magnetism. This relationship was discovered in 1831 by the English scientist Michael Faraday. He placed a wire between the poles of a magnet. When he moved the wire, an electric current flowed in it. The current is said to be induced in the wire. (*See* INDUCTION.) Between the poles of a magnet, there exists a magnetic field. Whenever a wire cuts a magnetic field, a current is induced. A current can also be induced by moving the magnet and keeping the wire still. This also causes the wire to cut the magnetic field.

Electricity is generated in power stations. From the power station, the electricity is sent along cables to homes and factories. The generators in a power station are usually driven by turbines. The turbines are themselves driven by steam, gas, or water. In most power stations, the turbine causes a large coil of wire to spin around inside a magnetic field. The coil is slotted into a metal drum. Together, they are called the armature. The magnetic field is supplied by a large elec-

Top: This power station controls the electrical flow to the island of Nantucket. © Michael Philip Manheim/The Stock Shop. Center left: This is the machine hall of a water-powered generating station. © Plessner International/The Stock Shop. Center right: The console in the foreground controls the turbo generator units of this coal-fired power station. © Terry Qing/FPG International. Bottom: Hospitals must have power at all times. This is a small generator used as a backup power supply in a modern hospital. © Tom Campbell/FPG International.

tromagnet. (*See* ELECTROMAGNETISM.) Each turn in the coil of wire produces an electric current. A large coil contains many turns. The current in each turn combines with the currents in the other turns to produce a large total current. The two ends of the coil are connected to one or two metal rings. The ring or rings are in contact with brushes. The brushes are rods made out of carbon.

AC and DC generators   There are two different types of electric current. They are called alternating current and direct current and are often abbreviated to AC and DC. A direct current flows in one direction only. An alternating current reverses its direction regularly. The current builds up in one direction and dies away again. Then it builds up in the other direction. Again it dies away and then builds up in the first direction again. This is called a cycle. In the United States, the alternating current that you have at home has 60 cycles a second. AC generators and DC generators have slightly different designs. The current produced in the coil is an alternating current. As the coil spins around, any part of the coil moves first one way and then the other through the magnetic field. As the coil spins around once, one cycle of alternating current is produced. In a DC generator, the alternating current is converted into direct current.

The wires from the coil in an AC generator are connected to two rings called slip rings. In a DC generator, the wires are connected to one ring that is split in half. This split ring is called a commutator. As the coil spins, the brushes touch each half of the commutator in turn. This causes the current to reverse its direction. But the current is already reversing its direction because it is an alternating current. The two effects cancel each other out. The current produced flows in one direction only and is a direct current.   M.E./J.T.

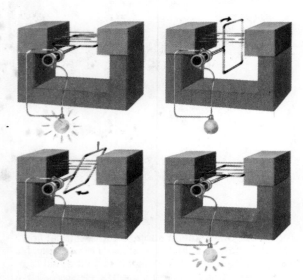

This generator consists of a loop of wire rotating in a magnetic field. An electric current is induced in the wire (top left) when it passes through the field. When it is not passing through the field, no current is induced (top right). As the rotating coil re-enters the field (bottom left), current again flows, reaching a maximum at the horizontal position.

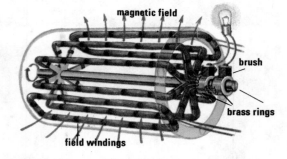

In large generators, there are many coils, called field windings. They insure that a constant current flows, since some windings are always passing through the magnetic field. Brass rings collect the current generated and pass it along via the brushes.